LEVELS

SET IN SOUL

THIS JOURNAL BELONGS TO

DEDICATED TO EVERY
NEW LEVEL WAITING
FOR ME

TABLE OF CONTENTS

HOW TO USE THIS JOURNAL

Levels is a journal that is created to help you focus and achieve your spiritual, physical, financial, emotional, career, social and relationship goals. This journal aids in helping you to make a decision in what you truly want for yourself and to then put in the spiritual, mental and physical work needed to achieving your goals. You have this journal because you realize it is time to do something different. It's time for you to focus and dedicate yourself to improving you. You realize that your achievements are not your own, so it is required of you to move into your next level. Your current level probably makes you uncomfortable. Any goal created to improve your current way of thinking, loving, living is a goal worth pursuing. Regardless of what has been said or what others believe, you can have everything that you want. EVERYTHING. There is nothing that is impossible for you. When God is the one you place your faith in, then you make faith like moves. Believe in God. Believe in yourself and make your goals a top priority. Let no struggle, obstacle or barrier keep you from your goal. Even when you make a mistake, you can still accomplish all that is within you. Use this journal to pace yourself and remind yourself of the level you are stepping into and what it is required of you.

It is recommended that you use this journal daily to practice the habit of focus and achieving. Using this journal daily will remind you that your goals are no longer something you are to put to the side, but to put on the top of your to do list. You are just that amazing and need to be reminded of the amazing things you can accomplish daily by sticking to your goals. With this Levels journal, it will cover the first six months of achieving what you seek out to do. Why six months? We believe that you would have formulated the habits needed to achieve your next level goals within six months. It's in the six months you will see drastic changes that this journal will aid in to keep you focused. There is a two month, four month and a final six month check in. Everyday set the goal....set the small goal to reach the bigger goal and go from there.

You will also see daily affirmations on the bottom of the page to aid you in feeling great about yourself and these goals. It is recommended that you repeat them to yourself out loud for one minute. Pay attention to your shift in attitude and actions. You will notice a difference. You deserve every new level you wish to rise up to. Love who you are becoming and enjoy the ride as you begin to achieve.

Your next level is ready for you.

NEW LEVEL
REQUIREMENTS
SPIRITUAL GOALS

Top Long Term Spiritual Goal:

Top Short Term Spiritual Goal:

What Motivated These Spiritual Goals?

What Purpose Do These Spiritual Goals Serve?

These Spiritual Goals Are Important To Me Because:

NEW LEVEL REQUIREMENTS

With A Renewed Mind, These Spiritual Goals Are:

I Have Been Trying To Achieve These Spiritual Goals Since:

What I Will Be Doing Differently To Achieve These Spiritual Goals:

Achieving These Spiritual Goals Will Make Me Feel:

What Is Required Of Me To Achieve These Spiritual Goals?

NEW LEVEL REQUIREMENTS

PHYSICAL GOALS

Top Long Term Physical Goal:

Top Short Term Physical Goal:

What Motivated These Physical Goals?

What Purpose Do These Physical Goals Serve?

These Physical Goals Are Important To Me Because:

NEW LEVEL REQUIREMENTS

With A Renewed Mind, These Physical Goals Are:

I Have Been Trying To Achieve These Physical Goals Since:

What I Will Be Doing Differently To Achieve These Physical Goals:

Achieving These Physical Goals Will Make Me Feel:

What Is Required Of Me To Achieve These Physical Goals?

FINANCIAL GOALS

Top Long Term Financial Goal:

Top Short Term Financial Goal:

What Motivated These Financial Goals?

What Purpose Do These Financial Goals Serve?

These Financial Goals Are Important To Me Because:

NEW LEVEL REQUIREMENTS

With A Renewed Mind, These Financial Goals Are:

I Have Been Trying To Achieve These Financial Goals Since:

What I Will Be Doing Differently To Achieve These Financial Goals:

Achieving These Financial Goals Will Make Me Feel:

What Is Required Of Me To Achieve These Financial Goals?

NEW LEVEL REQUIREMENTS

RELATIONSHIP GOALS

Top Long Term Relationship Goal:

Top Short Term Relationship Goal:

What Motivated These Relationship Goals?

What Purpose Do These Relationship Goals Serve?

These Relationship Goals Are Important To Me Because:

NEW LEVEL REQUIREMENTS

With A Renewed Mind, These Relationship Goals Are:

I Have Been Trying To Achieve These Relationship Goals Since:

What I Will Be Doing Differently To Achieve These Relationship Goals:

Achieving These Relationship Goals Will Make Me Feel:

What Is Required Of Me To Achieve These Relationship Goals?

NEW LEVEL REQUIREMENTS

CAREER GOALS

Top Long Term Career Goal:

Top Short Term Career Goal:

What Motivated These Career Goals?

What Purpose Do These Career Goals Serve?

These Career Goals Are Important To Me Because:

NEW LEVEL REQUIREMENTS

With A Renewed Mind, These Career Goals Are:

I Have Been Trying To Achieve These Career Goals Since:

What I Will Be Doing Differently To Achieve These Career Goals:

Achieving These Career Goals Will Make Me Feel:

What Is Required Of Me To Achieve These Career Goals?

NEW LEVEL REQUIREMENTS

EMOTIONAL GOALS

Top Long Term Emotional Goal:

Top Short Term Emotional Goal:

What Motivated These Emotional Goals?

What Purpose Do These Emotional Goals Serve?

These Emotional Goals Are Important To Me Because:

NEW LEVEL REQUIREMENTS

With A Renewed Mind, These Emotional Goals Are:

I Have Been Trying To Achieve These Emotional Goals Since:

What I Will Be Doing Differently To Achieve These Emotional Goals:

Achieving These Emotional Goals Will Make Me Feel:

What Is Required Of Me To Achieve These Emotional Goals?

NEW LEVEL REQUIREMENTS

<u>SOCIAL GOALS</u>

Top Long Term Social Goal:

Top Short Term Social Goal:

What Motivated These Social Goals?

What Purpose Do These Social Goals Serve?

These Social Goals Are Important To Me Because:

NEW LEVEL REQUIREMENTS

With A Renewed Mind, These Social Goals Are:

I Have Been Trying To Achieve These Social Goals Since:

What I Will Be Doing Differently To Achieve These Social Goals:

Achieving These Social Goals Will Make Me Feel:

What Is Required Of Me To Achieve These Social Goals?

STEPPING INTO A NEW LEVEL

LEVELS

Today: _____   Mood: _____

Ultimate Big Goal:

Today's Small Goal Towards The Ultimate Big Goal:

I Will Achieve This Goal Because:

Today I Am Doing This Towards My Goal:

The Spiritual Work I Did Towards My Big Goal:

The Mental Work I Did Towards My Big Goal:

The Physical Work I Did Today Towards My Big Goal:

It Takes _____ From Me To Achieve This Goal.

I Had To Start _____ So I Can_____.

And I Had To Stop _____So I Can_____.

I Will Not Quit My Goal Because:

LEVELS

Today: _____   Mood: _____

Ultimate Big Goal:

Today's Small Goal Towards The Ultimate Big Goal:

I Will Achieve This Goal Because:

Today I Am Doing This Towards My Goal:

The Spiritual Work I Did Towards My Big Goal:

The Mental Work I Did Towards My Big Goal:

The Physical Work I Did Today Towards My Big Goal:

It Takes _____ From Me To Achieve This Goal.

I Had To Start _____ So I Can_____.

And I Had To Stop _____So I Can_____.

I Will Not Quit My Goal Because:

Affirmation #2: The how doesn't matter because my why is powerful.

LEVELS

Today: Mood:

Ultimate Big Goal:

Today's Small Goal Towards The Ultimate Big Goal:

I Will Achieve This Goal Because:

Today I Am Doing This Towards My Goal:

The Spiritual Work I Did Towards My Big Goal:

The Mental Work I Did Towards My Big Goal:

The Physical Work I Did Today Towards My Big Goal:

It Takes _____ From Me To Achieve This Goal.

I Had To Start _____ So I Can_____.

And I Had To Stop _____So I Can_____.

I Will Not Quit My Goal Because:

LET NO ONE DISTRACT YOU FROM WHERE YOU ARE GOING.

LEVELS

Today: Mood:

Ultimate Big Goal:

Today's Small Goal Towards The Ultimate Big Goal:

I Will Achieve This Goal Because:

Today I Am Doing This Towards My Goal:

The Spiritual Work I Did Towards My Big Goal:

The Mental Work I Did Towards My Big Goal:

The Physical Work I Did Today Towards My Big Goal:

It Takes _____ From Me To Achieve This Goal.

I Had To Start _____ So I Can_____.

And I Had To Stop _____So I Can_____.

I Will Not Quit My Goal Because:

LEVELS

Today: Mood:

Ultimate Big Goal:

Today's Small Goal Towards The Ultimate Big Goal:

I Will Achieve This Goal Because:

Today I Am Doing This Towards My Goal:

The Spiritual Work I Did Towards My Big Goal:

The Mental Work I Did Towards My Big Goal:

The Physical Work I Did Today Towards My Big Goal:

It Takes _____ From Me To Achieve This Goal.

I Had To Start _____ So I Can_____.

And I Had To Stop _____So I Can_____.

I Will Not Quit My Goal Because:

LEVELS

Today: _____   Mood: _____

Ultimate Big Goal:

Today's Small Goal Towards The Ultimate Big Goal:

I Will Achieve This Goal Because:

Today I Am Doing This Towards My Goal:

The Spiritual Work I Did Towards My Big Goal:

The Mental Work I Did Towards My Big Goal:

The Physical Work I Did Today Towards My Big Goal:

It Takes _____ From Me To Achieve This Goal.

I Had To Start _____ So I Can_____.

And I Had To Stop _____So I Can_____.

I Will Not Quit My Goal Because:

LEVELS

Today: _____   Mood: _____

Ultimate Big Goal:

Today's Small Goal Towards The Ultimate Big Goal:

I Will Achieve This Goal Because:

Today I Am Doing This Towards My Goal:

The Spiritual Work I Did Towards My Big Goal:

The Mental Work I Did Towards My Big Goal:

The Physical Work I Did Today Towards My Big Goal:

It Takes _____ From Me To Achieve This Goal.

I Had To Start _____ So I Can_____.

And I Had To Stop _____So I Can_____.

I Will Not Quit My Goal Because:

LEVELS

Today: _____ Mood: _____

Ultimate Big Goal:

Today's Small Goal Towards The Ultimate Big Goal:

I Will Achieve This Goal Because:

Today I Am Doing This Towards My Goal:

The Spiritual Work I Did Towards My Big Goal:

The Mental Work I Did Towards My Big Goal:

The Physical Work I Did Today Towards My Big Goal:

It Takes _____ From Me To Achieve This Goal.

I Had To Start _____ So I Can_____.

And I Had To Stop _____So I Can_____.

I Will Not Quit My Goal Because:

LEVELS

Today: Mood:

Ultimate Big Goal:

Today's Small Goal Towards The Ultimate Big Goal:

I Will Achieve This Goal Because:

Today I Am Doing This Towards My Goal:

The Spiritual Work I Did Towards My Big Goal:

The Mental Work I Did Towards My Big Goal:

The Physical Work I Did Today Towards My Big Goal:

It Takes _____ From Me To Achieve This Goal.

I Had To Start _____ So I Can_____.

And I Had To Stop _____So I Can_____.

I Will Not Quit My Goal Because:

     Affirmation #9: A way is made for me everyday.

THERE IS NO STRUGGLE THAT WILL KEEP ME AWAY FROM WHAT BELONGS TO ME.

BECAUSE I REFUSE TO SETTLE FOR LESS, I WILL RECEIVE THE BEST.

LEVELS

Today: Mood:

Ultimate Big Goal:

Today's Small Goal Towards The Ultimate Big Goal:

I Will Achieve This Goal Because:

Today I Am Doing This Towards My Goal:

The Spiritual Work I Did Towards My Big Goal:

The Mental Work I Did Towards My Big Goal:

The Physical Work I Did Today Towards My Big Goal:

It Takes _____ From Me To Achieve This Goal.

I Had To Start _____ So I Can_____.

And I Had To Stop _____So I Can_____.

I Will Not Quit My Goal Because:

LEVELS

Today: Mood:

Ultimate Big Goal:

Today's Small Goal Towards The Ultimate Big Goal:

I Will Achieve This Goal Because:

Today I Am Doing This Towards My Goal:

The Spiritual Work I Did Towards My Big Goal:

The Mental Work I Did Towards My Big Goal:

The Physical Work I Did Today Towards My Big Goal:

It Takes _____ From Me To Achieve This Goal.

I Had To Start _____ So I Can_____.

And I Had To Stop _____So I Can_____.

I Will Not Quit My Goal Because:

LEVELS

Today: _____ Mood: _____

Ultimate Big Goal:

Today's Small Goal Towards The Ultimate Big Goal:

I Will Achieve This Goal Because:

Today I Am Doing This Towards My Goal:

The Spiritual Work I Did Towards My Big Goal:

The Mental Work I Did Towards My Big Goal:

The Physical Work I Did Today Towards My Big Goal:

It Takes _____ From Me To Achieve This Goal.

I Had To Start _____ So I Can_____.

And I Had To Stop _____So I Can_____.

I Will Not Quit My Goal Because:

LEVELS

Today: Mood:

Ultimate Big Goal:

Today's Small Goal Towards The Ultimate Big Goal:

I Will Achieve This Goal Because:

Today I Am Doing This Towards My Goal:

The Spiritual Work I Did Towards My Big Goal:

The Mental Work I Did Towards My Big Goal:

The Physical Work I Did Today Towards My Big Goal:

It Takes _____ From Me To Achieve This Goal.

I Had To Start _____ So I Can_____.

And I Had To Stop _____So I Can_____.

I Will Not Quit My Goal Because:

LEVELS

Today: Mood:

Ultimate Big Goal:

Today's Small Goal Towards The Ultimate Big Goal:

I Will Achieve This Goal Because:

Today I Am Doing This Towards My Goal:

The Spiritual Work I Did Towards My Big Goal:

The Mental Work I Did Towards My Big Goal:

The Physical Work I Did Today Towards My Big Goal:

It Takes _____ From Me To Achieve This Goal.

I Had To Start _____ So I Can_____.

And I Had To Stop _____So I Can_____.

I Will Not Quit My Goal Because:

LEVELS

Today: _____   Mood: _____

Ultimate Big Goal:

Today's Small Goal Towards The Ultimate Big Goal:

I Will Achieve This Goal Because:

Today I Am Doing This Towards My Goal:

The Spiritual Work I Did Towards My Big Goal:

The Mental Work I Did Towards My Big Goal:

The Physical Work I Did Today Towards My Big Goal:

It Takes _____ From Me To Achieve This Goal.

I Had To Start _____ So I Can_____.

And I Had To Stop _____So I Can_____.

I Will Not Quit My Goal Because:

LEVELS

Today: Mood:

Ultimate Big Goal:

Today's Small Goal Towards The Ultimate Big Goal:

I Will Achieve This Goal Because:

Today I Am Doing This Towards My Goal:

The Spiritual Work I Did Towards My Big Goal:

The Mental Work I Did Towards My Big Goal:

The Physical Work I Did Today Towards My Big Goal:

It Takes _____ From Me To Achieve This Goal.

I Had To Start _____ So I Can_____.

And I Had To Stop _____ So I Can_____.

I Will Not Quit My Goal Because:

LEVELS

Today: _____ Mood: _____

Ultimate Big Goal:

Today's Small Goal Towards The Ultimate Big Goal:

I Will Achieve This Goal Because:

Today I Am Doing This Towards My Goal:

The Spiritual Work I Did Towards My Big Goal:

The Mental Work I Did Towards My Big Goal:

The Physical Work I Did Today Towards My Big Goal:

It Takes _____ From Me To Achieve This Goal.

I Had To Start _____ So I Can_____.

And I Had To Stop _____So I Can_____.

I Will Not Quit My Goal Because:

I CAN ACHIEVE ANYTHING I PUT MY MIND TO.

LEVELS

Today: _____ Mood: _____

Ultimate Big Goal:

Today's Small Goal Towards The Ultimate Big Goal:

I Will Achieve This Goal Because:

Today I Am Doing This Towards My Goal:

The Spiritual Work I Did Towards My Big Goal:

The Mental Work I Did Towards My Big Goal:

The Physical Work I Did Today Towards My Big Goal:

It Takes _____ From Me To Achieve This Goal.

I Had To Start _____ So I Can_____.

And I Had To Stop _____So I Can_____.

I Will Not Quit My Goal Because:

LEVELS

Today: _____ Mood: _____

Ultimate Big Goal:

Today's Small Goal Towards The Ultimate Big Goal:

I Will Achieve This Goal Because:

Today I Am Doing This Towards My Goal:

The Spiritual Work I Did Towards My Big Goal:

The Mental Work I Did Towards My Big Goal:

The Physical Work I Did Today Towards My Big Goal:

It Takes _____ From Me To Achieve This Goal.

I Had To Start _____ So I Can_____.

And I Had To Stop _____So I Can_____.

I Will Not Quit My Goal Because:

LEVELS

Today: _____ Mood: _____

Ultimate Big Goal:

Today's Small Goal Towards The Ultimate Big Goal:

I Will Achieve This Goal Because:

Today I Am Doing This Towards My Goal:

The Spiritual Work I Did Towards My Big Goal:

The Mental Work I Did Towards My Big Goal:

The Physical Work I Did Today Towards My Big Goal:

It Takes _____ From Me To Achieve This Goal.

I Had To Start _____ So I Can_____.

And I Had To Stop _____So I Can_____.

I Will Not Quit My Goal Because:

LEVELS

Today: Mood:

Ultimate Big Goal:

Today's Small Goal Towards The Ultimate Big Goal:

I Will Achieve This Goal Because:

Today I Am Doing This Towards My Goal:

The Spiritual Work I Did Towards My Big Goal:

The Mental Work I Did Towards My Big Goal:

The Physical Work I Did Today Towards My Big Goal:

It Takes _____ From Me To Achieve This Goal.

I Had To Start _____ So I Can_____.

And I Had To Stop _____So I Can_____.

I Will Not Quit My Goal Because:

LEVELS

Today: _____   Mood: _____

Ultimate Big Goal:

Today's Small Goal Towards The Ultimate Big Goal:

I Will Achieve This Goal Because:

Today I Am Doing This Towards My Goal:

The Spiritual Work I Did Towards My Big Goal:

The Mental Work I Did Towards My Big Goal:

The Physical Work I Did Today Towards My Big Goal:

It Takes _____ From Me To Achieve This Goal.

I Had To Start _____ So I Can_____.

And I Had To Stop _____So I Can_____.

I Will Not Quit My Goal Because:

LEVELS

Today: Mood:

Ultimate Big Goal:

Today's Small Goal Towards The Ultimate Big Goal:

I Will Achieve This Goal Because:

Today I Am Doing This Towards My Goal:

The Spiritual Work I Did Towards My Big Goal:

The Mental Work I Did Towards My Big Goal:

The Physical Work I Did Today Towards My Big Goal:

It Takes _____ From Me To Achieve This Goal.

I Had To Start _____ So I Can_____.

And I Had To Stop _____So I Can_____.

I Will Not Quit My Goal Because:

LEVELS

Today: Mood:

Ultimate Big Goal:

Today's Small Goal Towards The Ultimate Big Goal:

I Will Achieve This Goal Because:

Today I Am Doing This Towards My Goal:

The Spiritual Work I Did Towards My Big Goal:

The Mental Work I Did Towards My Big Goal:

The Physical Work I Did Today Towards My Big Goal:

It Takes _____ From Me To Achieve This Goal.

I Had To Start _____ So I Can_____.

And I Had To Stop _____So I Can_____.

I Will Not Quit My Goal Because:

LEVELS

Today: _____   Mood: _____

Ultimate Big Goal:

Today's Small Goal Towards The Ultimate Big Goal:

I Will Achieve This Goal Because:

Today I Am Doing This Towards My Goal:

The Spiritual Work I Did Towards My Big Goal:

The Mental Work I Did Towards My Big Goal:

The Physical Work I Did Today Towards My Big Goal:

It Takes _____ From Me To Achieve This Goal.

I Had To Start _____ So I Can_____.

And I Had To Stop _____So I Can_____.

I Will Not Quit My Goal Because:

LEVELS

Today: Mood:

Ultimate Big Goal:

Today's Small Goal Towards The Ultimate Big Goal:

I Will Achieve This Goal Because:

Today I Am Doing This Towards My Goal:

The Spiritual Work I Did Towards My Big Goal:

The Mental Work I Did Towards My Big Goal:

The Physical Work I Did Today Towards My Big Goal:

It Takes _____ From Me To Achieve This Goal.

I Had To Start _____ So I Can_____.

And I Had To Stop _____So I Can_____.

I Will Not Quit My Goal Because:

LEVELS

Today: _____   Mood: _____

Ultimate Big Goal:

Today's Small Goal Towards The Ultimate Big Goal:

I Will Achieve This Goal Because:

Today I Am Doing This Towards My Goal:

The Spiritual Work I Did Towards My Big Goal:

The Mental Work I Did Towards My Big Goal:

The Physical Work I Did Today Towards My Big Goal:

It Takes _____ From Me To Achieve This Goal.

I Had To Start _____ So I Can_____.

And I Had To Stop _____So I Can_____.

I Will Not Quit My Goal Because:

LEVELS

Today: Mood:

Ultimate Big Goal:

Today's Small Goal Towards The Ultimate Big Goal:

I Will Achieve This Goal Because:

Today I Am Doing This Towards My Goal:

The Spiritual Work I Did Towards My Big Goal:

The Mental Work I Did Towards My Big Goal:

The Physical Work I Did Today Towards My Big Goal:

It Takes _____ From Me To Achieve This Goal.

I Had To Start _____ So I Can_____.

And I Had To Stop _____So I Can_____.

I Will Not Quit My Goal Because:

I AM.
I AM.
I AM.
I CAN.
I CAN.
I CAN.

LEVELS

Today: _____ Mood: _____

Ultimate Big Goal:

Today's Small Goal Towards The Ultimate Big Goal:

I Will Achieve This Goal Because:

Today I Am Doing This Towards My Goal:

The Spiritual Work I Did Towards My Big Goal:

The Mental Work I Did Towards My Big Goal:

The Physical Work I Did Today Towards My Big Goal:

It Takes _____ From Me To Achieve This Goal.

I Had To Start _____ So I Can_____.

And I Had To Stop _____So I Can_____.

I Will Not Quit My Goal Because:

LEVELS

Today: Mood:

Ultimate Big Goal:

Today's Small Goal Towards The Ultimate Big Goal:

I Will Achieve This Goal Because:

Today I Am Doing This Towards My Goal:

The Spiritual Work I Did Towards My Big Goal:

The Mental Work I Did Towards My Big Goal:

The Physical Work I Did Today Towards My Big Goal:

It Takes _____ From Me To Achieve This Goal.

I Had To Start _____ So I Can_____.

And I Had To Stop _____So I Can_____.

I Will Not Quit My Goal Because:

LEVELS

Today: Mood:

Ultimate Big Goal:

Today's Small Goal Towards The Ultimate Big Goal:

I Will Achieve This Goal Because:

Today I Am Doing This Towards My Goal:

The Spiritual Work I Did Towards My Big Goal:

The Mental Work I Did Towards My Big Goal:

The Physical Work I Did Today Towards My Big Goal:

It Takes _____ From Me To Achieve This Goal.

I Had To Start _____ So I Can_____.

And I Had To Stop _____So I Can_____.

I Will Not Quit My Goal Because:

LEVELS

Today: _____   Mood: _____

Ultimate Big Goal:

Today's Small Goal Towards The Ultimate Big Goal:

I Will Achieve This Goal Because:

Today I Am Doing This Towards My Goal:

The Spiritual Work I Did Towards My Big Goal:

The Mental Work I Did Towards My Big Goal:

The Physical Work I Did Today Towards My Big Goal:

It Takes _____ From Me To Achieve This Goal.

I Had To Start _____ So I Can_____.

And I Had To Stop _____So I Can_____.

I Will Not Quit My Goal Because:

LEVELS

Today: Mood:

Ultimate Big Goal:

Today's Small Goal Towards The Ultimate Big Goal:

I Will Achieve This Goal Because:

Today I Am Doing This Towards My Goal:

The Spiritual Work I Did Towards My Big Goal:

The Mental Work I Did Towards My Big Goal:

The Physical Work I Did Today Towards My Big Goal:

It Takes _____ From Me To Achieve This Goal.

I Had To Start _____ So I Can_____.

And I Had To Stop _____So I Can_____.

I Will Not Quit My Goal Because:

LEVELS

Today: Mood:

Ultimate Big Goal:

Today's Small Goal Towards The Ultimate Big Goal:

I Will Achieve This Goal Because:

Today I Am Doing This Towards My Goal:

The Spiritual Work I Did Towards My Big Goal:

The Mental Work I Did Towards My Big Goal:

The Physical Work I Did Today Towards My Big Goal:

It Takes _____ From Me To Achieve This Goal.

I Had To Start _____ So I Can_____.

And I Had To Stop _____So I Can_____.

I Will Not Quit My Goal Because:

LEVELS

Today: Mood:

Ultimate Big Goal:

Today's Small Goal Towards The Ultimate Big Goal:

I Will Achieve This Goal Because:

Today I Am Doing This Towards My Goal:

The Spiritual Work I Did Towards My Big Goal:

The Mental Work I Did Towards My Big Goal:

The Physical Work I Did Today Towards My Big Goal:

It Takes _____ From Me To Achieve This Goal.

I Had To Start _____ So I Can_____.

And I Had To Stop _____So I Can_____.

I Will Not Quit My Goal Because:

LEVELS

Today: Mood:

Ultimate Big Goal:

Today's Small Goal Towards The Ultimate Big Goal:

I Will Achieve This Goal Because:

Today I Am Doing This Towards My Goal:

The Spiritual Work I Did Towards My Big Goal:

The Mental Work I Did Towards My Big Goal:

The Physical Work I Did Today Towards My Big Goal:

It Takes _____ From Me To Achieve This Goal.

I Had To Start _____ So I Can_____.

And I Had To Stop _____So I Can_____.

I Will Not Quit My Goal Because:

LEVELS

Today: Mood:

Ultimate Big Goal:

Today's Small Goal Towards The Ultimate Big Goal:

I Will Achieve This Goal Because:

Today I Am Doing This Towards My Goal:

The Spiritual Work I Did Towards My Big Goal:

The Mental Work I Did Towards My Big Goal:

The Physical Work I Did Today Towards My Big Goal:

It Takes _____ From Me To Achieve This Goal.

I Had To Start _____ So I Can_____.

And I Had To Stop _____So I Can_____.

I Will Not Quit My Goal Because:

LEVELS

Today: _____   Mood: _____

Ultimate Big Goal:

Today's Small Goal Towards The Ultimate Big Goal:

I Will Achieve This Goal Because:

Today I Am Doing This Towards My Goal:

The Spiritual Work I Did Towards My Big Goal:

The Mental Work I Did Towards My Big Goal:

The Physical Work I Did Today Towards My Big Goal:

It Takes _____ From Me To Achieve This Goal.

I Had To Start _____ So I Can_____.

And I Had To Stop _____So I Can_____.

I Will Not Quit My Goal Because:

LEVELS

Today: _____   Mood: _____

Ultimate Big Goal:

Today's Small Goal Towards The Ultimate Big Goal:

I Will Achieve This Goal Because:

Today I Am Doing This Towards My Goal:

The Spiritual Work I Did Towards My Big Goal:

The Mental Work I Did Towards My Big Goal:

The Physical Work I Did Today Towards My Big Goal:

It Takes _____ From Me To Achieve This Goal.

I Had To Start _____ So I Can_____.

And I Had To Stop _____So I Can_____.

I Will Not Quit My Goal Because:

LEVELS

Today: _____   Mood: _____

Ultimate Big Goal:

Today's Small Goal Towards The Ultimate Big Goal:

I Will Achieve This Goal Because:

Today I Am Doing This Towards My Goal:

The Spiritual Work I Did Towards My Big Goal:

The Mental Work I Did Towards My Big Goal:

The Physical Work I Did Today Towards My Big Goal:

It Takes _____ From Me To Achieve This Goal.

I Had To Start _____ So I Can_____.

And I Had To Stop _____So I Can_____.

I Will Not Quit My Goal Because:

LEVELS

Today: Mood:

Ultimate Big Goal:

Today's Small Goal Towards The Ultimate Big Goal:

I Will Achieve This Goal Because:

Today I Am Doing This Towards My Goal:

The Spiritual Work I Did Towards My Big Goal:

The Mental Work I Did Towards My Big Goal:

The Physical Work I Did Today Towards My Big Goal:

It Takes _____ From Me To Achieve This Goal.

I Had To Start _____ So I Can_____.

And I Had To Stop _____So I Can_____.

I Will Not Quit My Goal Because:

Affirmation #41: Everything I touch turns into gold.

LEVELS

Today: _____ Mood: _____

Ultimate Big Goal:

Today's Small Goal Towards The Ultimate Big Goal:

I Will Achieve This Goal Because:

Today I Am Doing This Towards My Goal:

The Spiritual Work I Did Towards My Big Goal:

The Mental Work I Did Towards My Big Goal:

The Physical Work I Did Today Towards My Big Goal:

It Takes _____ From Me To Achieve This Goal.

I Had To Start _____ So I Can_____.

And I Had To Stop _____So I Can_____.

I Will Not Quit My Goal Because:

LEVELS

Today: _____   Mood: _____

Ultimate Big Goal:

Today's Small Goal Towards The Ultimate Big Goal:

I Will Achieve This Goal Because:

Today I Am Doing This Towards My Goal:

The Spiritual Work I Did Towards My Big Goal:

The Mental Work I Did Towards My Big Goal:

The Physical Work I Did Today Towards My Big Goal:

It Takes _____ From Me To Achieve This Goal.

I Had To Start _____ So I Can_____.

And I Had To Stop _____So I Can_____.

I Will Not Quit My Goal Because:

LEVELS

Today: Mood:

Ultimate Big Goal:

Today's Small Goal Towards The Ultimate Big Goal:

I Will Achieve This Goal Because:

Today I Am Doing This Towards My Goal:

The Spiritual Work I Did Towards My Big Goal:

The Mental Work I Did Towards My Big Goal:

The Physical Work I Did Today Towards My Big Goal:

It Takes _____ From Me To Achieve This Goal.

I Had To Start _____ So I Can_____.

And I Had To Stop _____So I Can_____.

I Will Not Quit My Goal Because:

LEVELS

Today: _____   Mood: _____

Ultimate Big Goal:

Today's Small Goal Towards The Ultimate Big Goal:

I Will Achieve This Goal Because:

Today I Am Doing This Towards My Goal:

The Spiritual Work I Did Towards My Big Goal:

The Mental Work I Did Towards My Big Goal:

The Physical Work I Did Today Towards My Big Goal:

It Takes _____ From Me To Achieve This Goal.

I Had To Start _____ So I Can_____.

And I Had To Stop _____So I Can_____.

I Will Not Quit My Goal Because:

LEVELS

Today: _____   Mood: _____

Ultimate Big Goal:

Today's Small Goal Towards The Ultimate Big Goal:

I Will Achieve This Goal Because:

Today I Am Doing This Towards My Goal:

The Spiritual Work I Did Towards My Big Goal:

The Mental Work I Did Towards My Big Goal:

The Physical Work I Did Today Towards My Big Goal:

It Takes _____ From Me To Achieve This Goal.

I Had To Start _____ So I Can_____.

And I Had To Stop _____So I Can_____.

I Will Not Quit My Goal Because:

NOT EVERYONE CAN BE PART OF THE MASTER PLAN.

LEVELS

Today: _____ Mood: _____

Ultimate Big Goal:

Today's Small Goal Towards The Ultimate Big Goal:

I Will Achieve This Goal Because:

Today I Am Doing This Towards My Goal:

The Spiritual Work I Did Towards My Big Goal:

The Mental Work I Did Towards My Big Goal:

The Physical Work I Did Today Towards My Big Goal:

It Takes _____ From Me To Achieve This Goal.

I Had To Start _____ So I Can_____.

And I Had To Stop _____So I Can_____.

I Will Not Quit My Goal Because:

LEVELS

Today: _____ Mood: _____

Ultimate Big Goal:

Today's Small Goal Towards The Ultimate Big Goal:

I Will Achieve This Goal Because:

Today I Am Doing This Towards My Goal:

The Spiritual Work I Did Towards My Big Goal:

The Mental Work I Did Towards My Big Goal:

The Physical Work I Did Today Towards My Big Goal:

It Takes _____ From Me To Achieve This Goal.

I Had To Start _____ So I Can_____.

And I Had To Stop _____So I Can_____.

I Will Not Quit My Goal Because:

Affirmation #48: I am living the dream.

LEVELS

Today: Mood:

Ultimate Big Goal:

Today's Small Goal Towards The Ultimate Big Goal:

I Will Achieve This Goal Because:

Today I Am Doing This Towards My Goal:

The Spiritual Work I Did Towards My Big Goal:

The Mental Work I Did Towards My Big Goal:

The Physical Work I Did Today Towards My Big Goal:

It Takes _____ From Me To Achieve This Goal.

I Had To Start _____ So I Can_____.

And I Had To Stop _____So I Can_____.

I Will Not Quit My Goal Because:

LEVELS

Today: _____ Mood: _____

Ultimate Big Goal:

Today's Small Goal Towards The Ultimate Big Goal:

I Will Achieve This Goal Because:

Today I Am Doing This Towards My Goal:

The Spiritual Work I Did Towards My Big Goal:

The Mental Work I Did Towards My Big Goal:

The Physical Work I Did Today Towards My Big Goal:

It Takes _____ From Me To Achieve This Goal.

I Had To Start _____ So I Can_____.

And I Had To Stop _____So I Can_____.

I Will Not Quit My Goal Because:

LEVELS

Today: Mood:

Ultimate Big Goal:

Today's Small Goal Towards The Ultimate Big Goal:

I Will Achieve This Goal Because:

Today I Am Doing This Towards My Goal:

The Spiritual Work I Did Towards My Big Goal:

The Mental Work I Did Towards My Big Goal:

The Physical Work I Did Today Towards My Big Goal:

It Takes _____ From Me To Achieve This Goal.

I Had To Start _____ So I Can_____.

And I Had To Stop _____So I Can_____.

I Will Not Quit My Goal Because:

I GET BIG RESULTS BECAUSE I THINK BIG.

LEVELS

Today: Mood:

Ultimate Big Goal:

Today's Small Goal Towards The Ultimate Big Goal:

I Will Achieve This Goal Because:

Today I Am Doing This Towards My Goal:

The Spiritual Work I Did Towards My Big Goal:

The Mental Work I Did Towards My Big Goal:

The Physical Work I Did Today Towards My Big Goal:

It Takes _____ From Me To Achieve This Goal.

I Had To Start _____ So I Can_____.

And I Had To Stop _____So I Can_____.

I Will Not Quit My Goal Because:

LEVELS

Today: Mood:

Ultimate Big Goal:

Today's Small Goal Towards The Ultimate Big Goal:

I Will Achieve This Goal Because:

Today I Am Doing This Towards My Goal:

The Spiritual Work I Did Towards My Big Goal:

The Mental Work I Did Towards My Big Goal:

The Physical Work I Did Today Towards My Big Goal:

It Takes _____ From Me To Achieve This Goal.

I Had To Start _____ So I Can_____.

And I Had To Stop _____So I Can_____.

I Will Not Quit My Goal Because:

Affirmation #53: I am naturally loved everywhere that I go.

LEVELS

Today: _____ Mood: _____

Ultimate Big Goal:

Today's Small Goal Towards The Ultimate Big Goal:

I Will Achieve This Goal Because:

Today I Am Doing This Towards My Goal:

The Spiritual Work I Did Towards My Big Goal:

The Mental Work I Did Towards My Big Goal:

The Physical Work I Did Today Towards My Big Goal:

It Takes _____ From Me To Achieve This Goal.

I Had To Start _____ So I Can_____.

And I Had To Stop _____So I Can_____.

I Will Not Quit My Goal Because:

LEVELS

Today: _____   Mood: _____

Ultimate Big Goal:

Today's Small Goal Towards The Ultimate Big Goal:

I Will Achieve This Goal Because:

Today I Am Doing This Towards My Goal:

The Spiritual Work I Did Towards My Big Goal:

The Mental Work I Did Towards My Big Goal:

The Physical Work I Did Today Towards My Big Goal:

It Takes _____ From Me To Achieve This Goal.

I Had To Start _____ So I Can_____.

And I Had To Stop _____So I Can_____.

I Will Not Quit My Goal Because:

LEVELS

Today: Mood:

Ultimate Big Goal:

Today's Small Goal Towards The Ultimate Big Goal:

I Will Achieve This Goal Because:

Today I Am Doing This Towards My Goal:

The Spiritual Work I Did Towards My Big Goal:

The Mental Work I Did Towards My Big Goal:

The Physical Work I Did Today Towards My Big Goal:

It Takes _____ From Me To Achieve This Goal.

I Had To Start _____ So I Can_____.

And I Had To Stop _____So I Can_____.

I Will Not Quit My Goal Because:

LEVELS

Today: _____ Mood: _____

Ultimate Big Goal:

Today's Small Goal Towards The Ultimate Big Goal:

I Will Achieve This Goal Because:

Today I Am Doing This Towards My Goal:

The Spiritual Work I Did Towards My Big Goal:

The Mental Work I Did Towards My Big Goal:

The Physical Work I Did Today Towards My Big Goal:

It Takes _____ From Me To Achieve This Goal.

I Had To Start _____ So I Can_____.

And I Had To Stop _____So I Can_____.

I Will Not Quit My Goal Because:

Affirmation #57: I love the feeling of being in love.

MY GOALS ARE MY PRIORITY.

LEVELS

Today: Mood:

Ultimate Big Goal:

Today's Small Goal Towards The Ultimate Big Goal:

I Will Achieve This Goal Because:

Today I Am Doing This Towards My Goal:

The Spiritual Work I Did Towards My Big Goal:

The Mental Work I Did Towards My Big Goal:

The Physical Work I Did Today Towards My Big Goal:

It Takes _____ From Me To Achieve This Goal.

I Had To Start _____ So I Can_____.

And I Had To Stop _____So I Can_____.

I Will Not Quit My Goal Because:

LEVELS

Today: _____   Mood: _____

Ultimate Big Goal:

Today's Small Goal Towards The Ultimate Big Goal:

I Will Achieve This Goal Because:

Today I Am Doing This Towards My Goal:

The Spiritual Work I Did Towards My Big Goal:

The Mental Work I Did Towards My Big Goal:

The Physical Work I Did Today Towards My Big Goal:

It Takes _____ From Me To Achieve This Goal.

I Had To Start _____ So I Can_____.

And I Had To Stop _____So I Can_____.

I Will Not Quit My Goal Because:

LEVELS

Today: _____ Mood: _____

Ultimate Big Goal:

Today's Small Goal Towards The Ultimate Big Goal:

I Will Achieve This Goal Because:

Today I Am Doing This Towards My Goal:

The Spiritual Work I Did Towards My Big Goal:

The Mental Work I Did Towards My Big Goal:

The Physical Work I Did Today Towards My Big Goal:

It Takes _____ From Me To Achieve This Goal.

I Had To Start _____ So I Can_____.

And I Had To Stop _____So I Can_____.

I Will Not Quit My Goal Because:

TWO MONTH CHECK IN !!!!

WHAT HAVE YOU ACCOMPLISHED?

HOW DO YOU FEEL?

NOT WHERE YOU WANT? GET TO WORK !!!

LEVELS

Today: Mood:

Ultimate Big Goal:

Today's Small Goal Towards The Ultimate Big Goal:

I Will Achieve This Goal Because:

Today I Am Doing This Towards My Goal:

The Spiritual Work I Did Towards My Big Goal:

The Mental Work I Did Towards My Big Goal:

The Physical Work I Did Today Towards My Big Goal:

It Takes _____ From Me To Achieve This Goal.

I Had To Start _____ So I Can_____.

And I Had To Stop _____So I Can_____.

I Will Not Quit My Goal Because:

LEVELS

Today: Mood:

Ultimate Big Goal:

Today's Small Goal Towards The Ultimate Big Goal:

I Will Achieve This Goal Because:

Today I Am Doing This Towards My Goal:

The Spiritual Work I Did Towards My Big Goal:

The Mental Work I Did Towards My Big Goal:

The Physical Work I Did Today Towards My Big Goal:

It Takes _____ From Me To Achieve This Goal.

I Had To Start _____ So I Can_____.

And I Had To Stop _____So I Can_____.

I Will Not Quit My Goal Because:

LEVELS

Today: _____   Mood: _____

Ultimate Big Goal:

Today's Small Goal Towards The Ultimate Big Goal:

I Will Achieve This Goal Because:

Today I Am Doing This Towards My Goal:

The Spiritual Work I Did Towards My Big Goal:

The Mental Work I Did Towards My Big Goal:

The Physical Work I Did Today Towards My Big Goal:

It Takes _____ From Me To Achieve This Goal.

I Had To Start _____ So I Can_____.

And I Had To Stop _____So I Can_____.

I Will Not Quit My Goal Because:

LEVELS

Today: Mood:

Ultimate Big Goal:

Today's Small Goal Towards The Ultimate Big Goal:

I Will Achieve This Goal Because:

Today I Am Doing This Towards My Goal:

The Spiritual Work I Did Towards My Big Goal:

The Mental Work I Did Towards My Big Goal:

The Physical Work I Did Today Towards My Big Goal:

It Takes _____ From Me To Achieve This Goal.

I Had To Start _____ So I Can_____.

And I Had To Stop _____So I Can_____.

I Will Not Quit My Goal Because:

LEVELS

Today: _____ Mood: _____

Ultimate Big Goal:

Today's Small Goal Towards The Ultimate Big Goal:

I Will Achieve This Goal Because:

Today I Am Doing This Towards My Goal:

The Spiritual Work I Did Towards My Big Goal:

The Mental Work I Did Towards My Big Goal:

The Physical Work I Did Today Towards My Big Goal:

It Takes _____ From Me To Achieve This Goal.

I Had To Start _____ So I Can_____.

And I Had To Stop _____So I Can_____.

I Will Not Quit My Goal Because:

Affirmation #65: I am proud of my inner peace.

IN EVERYTHING, THERE ARE LEVELS.

LEVELS

Today: Mood:

Ultimate Big Goal:

Today's Small Goal Towards The Ultimate Big Goal:

I Will Achieve This Goal Because:

Today I Am Doing This Towards My Goal:

The Spiritual Work I Did Towards My Big Goal:

The Mental Work I Did Towards My Big Goal:

The Physical Work I Did Today Towards My Big Goal:

It Takes _____ From Me To Achieve This Goal.

I Had To Start _____ So I Can_____.

And I Had To Stop _____So I Can_____.

I Will Not Quit My Goal Because:

     Affirmation #66: I respond peacefully in every situation.

LEVELS

Today: Mood:

Ultimate Big Goal:

Today's Small Goal Towards The Ultimate Big Goal:

I Will Achieve This Goal Because:

Today I Am Doing This Towards My Goal:

The Spiritual Work I Did Towards My Big Goal:

The Mental Work I Did Towards My Big Goal:

The Physical Work I Did Today Towards My Big Goal:

It Takes _____ From Me To Achieve This Goal.

I Had To Start _____ So I Can_____.

And I Had To Stop _____So I Can_____.

I Will Not Quit My Goal Because:

LEVELS

Today: Mood:

Ultimate Big Goal:

Today's Small Goal Towards The Ultimate Big Goal:

I Will Achieve This Goal Because:

Today I Am Doing This Towards My Goal:

The Spiritual Work I Did Towards My Big Goal:

The Mental Work I Did Towards My Big Goal:

The Physical Work I Did Today Towards My Big Goal:

It Takes _____ From Me To Achieve This Goal.

I Had To Start _____ So I Can_____.

And I Had To Stop _____ So I Can_____.

I Will Not Quit My Goal Because:

I WILL LIVE IN EXCELLENCE.

LEVELS

Today: Mood:

Ultimate Big Goal:

Today's Small Goal Towards The Ultimate Big Goal:

I Will Achieve This Goal Because:

Today I Am Doing This Towards My Goal:

The Spiritual Work I Did Towards My Big Goal:

The Mental Work I Did Towards My Big Goal:

The Physical Work I Did Today Towards My Big Goal:

It Takes _____ From Me To Achieve This Goal.

I Had To Start _____ So I Can_____.

And I Had To Stop _____So I Can_____.

I Will Not Quit My Goal Because:

LEVELS

Today: Mood:

Ultimate Big Goal:

Today's Small Goal Towards The Ultimate Big Goal:

I Will Achieve This Goal Because:

Today I Am Doing This Towards My Goal:

The Spiritual Work I Did Towards My Big Goal:

The Mental Work I Did Towards My Big Goal:

The Physical Work I Did Today Towards My Big Goal:

It Takes _____ From Me To Achieve This Goal.

I Had To Start _____ So I Can_____.

And I Had To Stop _____So I Can_____.

I Will Not Quit My Goal Because:

LEVELS

Today: Mood:

Ultimate Big Goal:

Today's Small Goal Towards The Ultimate Big Goal:

I Will Achieve This Goal Because:

Today I Am Doing This Towards My Goal:

The Spiritual Work I Did Towards My Big Goal:

The Mental Work I Did Towards My Big Goal:

The Physical Work I Did Today Towards My Big Goal:

It Takes _____ From Me To Achieve This Goal.

I Had To Start _____ So I Can_____.

And I Had To Stop _____So I Can_____.

I Will Not Quit My Goal Because:

Affirmation #71: I accept all experiences.

LEVELS

Today: _____ Mood: _____

Ultimate Big Goal:

Today's Small Goal Towards The Ultimate Big Goal:

I Will Achieve This Goal Because:

Today I Am Doing This Towards My Goal:

The Spiritual Work I Did Towards My Big Goal:

The Mental Work I Did Towards My Big Goal:

The Physical Work I Did Today Towards My Big Goal:

It Takes _____ From Me To Achieve This Goal.

I Had To Start _____ So I Can_____.

And I Had To Stop _____So I Can_____.

I Will Not Quit My Goal Because:

LEVELS

Today: _____ Mood: _____

Ultimate Big Goal:

Today's Small Goal Towards The Ultimate Big Goal:

I Will Achieve This Goal Because:

Today I Am Doing This Towards My Goal:

The Spiritual Work I Did Towards My Big Goal:

The Mental Work I Did Towards My Big Goal:

The Physical Work I Did Today Towards My Big Goal:

It Takes _____ From Me To Achieve This Goal.

I Had To Start _____ So I Can_____.

And I Had To Stop _____So I Can_____.

I Will Not Quit My Goal Because:

Affirmation #73: My body and mind is healing every single day.

LEVELS

Today: Mood:

Ultimate Big Goal:

Today's Small Goal Towards The Ultimate Big Goal:

I Will Achieve This Goal Because:

Today I Am Doing This Towards My Goal:

The Spiritual Work I Did Towards My Big Goal:

The Mental Work I Did Towards My Big Goal:

The Physical Work I Did Today Towards My Big Goal:

It Takes _____ From Me To Achieve This Goal.

I Had To Start _____ So I Can_____.

And I Had To Stop _____So I Can_____.

I Will Not Quit My Goal Because:

LEVELS

Today: Mood:

Ultimate Big Goal:

Today's Small Goal Towards The Ultimate Big Goal:

I Will Achieve This Goal Because:

Today I Am Doing This Towards My Goal:

The Spiritual Work I Did Towards My Big Goal:

The Mental Work I Did Towards My Big Goal:

The Physical Work I Did Today Towards My Big Goal:

It Takes _____ From Me To Achieve This Goal.

I Had To Start _____ So I Can_____.

And I Had To Stop _____So I Can_____.

I Will Not Quit My Goal Because:

        Affirmation #75: My body is full of energy.

I AM BETTER THAN I WAS YESTERDAY.

I BELIEVE IN MY DREAMS.

LEVELS

Today: _____   Mood: _____

Ultimate Big Goal:

Today's Small Goal Towards The Ultimate Big Goal:

I Will Achieve This Goal Because:

Today I Am Doing This Towards My Goal:

The Spiritual Work I Did Towards My Big Goal:

The Mental Work I Did Towards My Big Goal:

The Physical Work I Did Today Towards My Big Goal:

It Takes _____ From Me To Achieve This Goal.

I Had To Start _____ So I Can_____.

And I Had To Stop _____So I Can_____.

I Will Not Quit My Goal Because:

LEVELS

Today: _____ Mood: _____

Ultimate Big Goal:

Today's Small Goal Towards The Ultimate Big Goal:

I Will Achieve This Goal Because:

Today I Am Doing This Towards My Goal:

The Spiritual Work I Did Towards My Big Goal:

The Mental Work I Did Towards My Big Goal:

The Physical Work I Did Today Towards My Big Goal:

It Takes _____ From Me To Achieve This Goal.

I Had To Start _____ So I Can_____.

And I Had To Stop _____So I Can_____.

I Will Not Quit My Goal Because:

Affirmation #77: My immune system is very strong.

LEVELS

Today: Mood:

Ultimate Big Goal:

Today's Small Goal Towards The Ultimate Big Goal:

I Will Achieve This Goal Because:

Today I Am Doing This Towards My Goal:

The Spiritual Work I Did Towards My Big Goal:

The Mental Work I Did Towards My Big Goal:

The Physical Work I Did Today Towards My Big Goal:

It Takes _____ From Me To Achieve This Goal.

I Had To Start _____ So I Can_____.

And I Had To Stop _____So I Can_____.

I Will Not Quit My Goal Because:

LEVELS

Today: _____ Mood: _____

Ultimate Big Goal:

Today's Small Goal Towards The Ultimate Big Goal:

I Will Achieve This Goal Because:

Today I Am Doing This Towards My Goal:

The Spiritual Work I Did Towards My Big Goal:

The Mental Work I Did Towards My Big Goal:

The Physical Work I Did Today Towards My Big Goal:

It Takes _____ From Me To Achieve This Goal.

I Had To Start _____ So I Can_____.

And I Had To Stop _____So I Can_____.

I Will Not Quit My Goal Because:

LEVELS

Today: _____ Mood: _____

Ultimate Big Goal:

Today's Small Goal Towards The Ultimate Big Goal:

I Will Achieve This Goal Because:

Today I Am Doing This Towards My Goal:

The Spiritual Work I Did Towards My Big Goal:

The Mental Work I Did Towards My Big Goal:

The Physical Work I Did Today Towards My Big Goal:

It Takes _____ From Me To Achieve This Goal.

I Had To Start _____ So I Can_____.

And I Had To Stop _____So I Can_____.

I Will Not Quit My Goal Because:

LEVELS

Today: Mood:

Ultimate Big Goal:

Today's Small Goal Towards The Ultimate Big Goal:

I Will Achieve This Goal Because:

Today I Am Doing This Towards My Goal:

The Spiritual Work I Did Towards My Big Goal:

The Mental Work I Did Towards My Big Goal:

The Physical Work I Did Today Towards My Big Goal:

It Takes _____ From Me To Achieve This Goal.

I Had To Start _____ So I Can_____.

And I Had To Stop _____So I Can_____.

I Will Not Quit My Goal Because:

LEVELS

Today: _____   Mood: _____

Ultimate Big Goal:

Today's Small Goal Towards The Ultimate Big Goal:

I Will Achieve This Goal Because:

Today I Am Doing This Towards My Goal:

The Spiritual Work I Did Towards My Big Goal:

The Mental Work I Did Towards My Big Goal:

The Physical Work I Did Today Towards My Big Goal:

It Takes _____ From Me To Achieve This Goal.

I Had To Start _____ So I Can_____.

And I Had To Stop _____So I Can_____.

I Will Not Quit My Goal Because:

LEVELS

Today: _____ Mood: _____

Ultimate Big Goal:

Today's Small Goal Towards The Ultimate Big Goal:

I Will Achieve This Goal Because:

Today I Am Doing This Towards My Goal:

The Spiritual Work I Did Towards My Big Goal:

The Mental Work I Did Towards My Big Goal:

The Physical Work I Did Today Towards My Big Goal:

It Takes _____ From Me To Achieve This Goal.

I Had To Start _____ So I Can_____.

And I Had To Stop _____So I Can_____.

I Will Not Quit My Goal Because:

Affirmation #83: I believe that my God will guide me to the right decision.

MY GOALS ARE MY PRIORITY.

LEVELS

Today: Mood:

Ultimate Big Goal:

Today's Small Goal Towards The Ultimate Big Goal:

I Will Achieve This Goal Because:

Today I Am Doing This Towards My Goal:

The Spiritual Work I Did Towards My Big Goal:

The Mental Work I Did Towards My Big Goal:

The Physical Work I Did Today Towards My Big Goal:

It Takes _____ From Me To Achieve This Goal.

I Had To Start _____ So I Can_____.

And I Had To Stop _____So I Can_____.

I Will Not Quit My Goal Because:

LEVELS

Today: Mood:

Ultimate Big Goal:

Today's Small Goal Towards The Ultimate Big Goal:

I Will Achieve This Goal Because:

Today I Am Doing This Towards My Goal:

The Spiritual Work I Did Towards My Big Goal:

The Mental Work I Did Towards My Big Goal:

The Physical Work I Did Today Towards My Big Goal:

It Takes _____ From Me To Achieve This Goal.

I Had To Start _____ So I Can_____.

And I Had To Stop _____So I Can_____.

I Will Not Quit My Goal Because:

LEVELS

Today: Mood:

Ultimate Big Goal:

Today's Small Goal Towards The Ultimate Big Goal:

I Will Achieve This Goal Because:

Today I Am Doing This Towards My Goal:

The Spiritual Work I Did Towards My Big Goal:

The Mental Work I Did Towards My Big Goal:

The Physical Work I Did Today Towards My Big Goal:

It Takes _____ From Me To Achieve This Goal.

I Had To Start _____ So I Can_____.

And I Had To Stop _____So I Can_____.

I Will Not Quit My Goal Because:

LEVELS

Today: Mood:

Ultimate Big Goal:

Today's Small Goal Towards The Ultimate Big Goal:

I Will Achieve This Goal Because:

Today I Am Doing This Towards My Goal:

The Spiritual Work I Did Towards My Big Goal:

The Mental Work I Did Towards My Big Goal:

The Physical Work I Did Today Towards My Big Goal:

It Takes _____ From Me To Achieve This Goal.

I Had To Start _____ So I Can_____.

And I Had To Stop _____So I Can_____.

I Will Not Quit My Goal Because:

LEVELS

Today: _____   Mood: _____

Ultimate Big Goal:

Today's Small Goal Towards The Ultimate Big Goal:

I Will Achieve This Goal Because:

Today I Am Doing This Towards My Goal:

The Spiritual Work I Did Towards My Big Goal:

The Mental Work I Did Towards My Big Goal:

The Physical Work I Did Today Towards My Big Goal:

It Takes _____ From Me To Achieve This Goal.

I Had To Start _____ So I Can_____.

And I Had To Stop _____So I Can_____.

I Will Not Quit My Goal Because:

LEVELS

Today: _____   Mood: _____

Ultimate Big Goal:

Today's Small Goal Towards The Ultimate Big Goal:

I Will Achieve This Goal Because:

Today I Am Doing This Towards My Goal:

The Spiritual Work I Did Towards My Big Goal:

The Mental Work I Did Towards My Big Goal:

The Physical Work I Did Today Towards My Big Goal:

It Takes _____ From Me To Achieve This Goal.

I Had To Start _____ So I Can_____.

And I Had To Stop _____So I Can_____.

I Will Not Quit My Goal Because:

NO ONE'S OPINION ABOUT MY GOALS MATTER.

LEVELS

Today: Mood:

Ultimate Big Goal:

Today's Small Goal Towards The Ultimate Big Goal:

I Will Achieve This Goal Because:

Today I Am Doing This Towards My Goal:

The Spiritual Work I Did Towards My Big Goal:

The Mental Work I Did Towards My Big Goal:

The Physical Work I Did Today Towards My Big Goal:

It Takes _____ From Me To Achieve This Goal.

I Had To Start _____ So I Can_____.

And I Had To Stop _____So I Can_____.

I Will Not Quit My Goal Because:

LEVELS

Today: Mood:

Ultimate Big Goal:

Today's Small Goal Towards The Ultimate Big Goal:

I Will Achieve This Goal Because:

Today I Am Doing This Towards My Goal:

The Spiritual Work I Did Towards My Big Goal:

The Mental Work I Did Towards My Big Goal:

The Physical Work I Did Today Towards My Big Goal:

It Takes _____ From Me To Achieve This Goal.

I Had To Start _____ So I Can_____.

And I Had To Stop _____So I Can_____.

I Will Not Quit My Goal Because:

Affirmation #91: I have so much hope today.

LEVELS

Today: Mood:

Ultimate Big Goal:

Today's Small Goal Towards The Ultimate Big Goal:

I Will Achieve This Goal Because:

Today I Am Doing This Towards My Goal:

The Spiritual Work I Did Towards My Big Goal:

The Mental Work I Did Towards My Big Goal:

The Physical Work I Did Today Towards My Big Goal:

It Takes _____ From Me To Achieve This Goal.

I Had To Start _____ So I Can_____.

And I Had To Stop _____So I Can_____.

I Will Not Quit My Goal Because:

LEVELS

Today: _____ Mood: _____

Ultimate Big Goal:

Today's Small Goal Towards The Ultimate Big Goal:

I Will Achieve This Goal Because:

Today I Am Doing This Towards My Goal:

The Spiritual Work I Did Towards My Big Goal:

The Mental Work I Did Towards My Big Goal:

The Physical Work I Did Today Towards My Big Goal:

It Takes _____ From Me To Achieve This Goal.

I Had To Start _____ So I Can_____.

And I Had To Stop _____So I Can_____.

I Will Not Quit My Goal Because:

LEVELS

Today: _____   Mood: _____

Ultimate Big Goal:

Today's Small Goal Towards The Ultimate Big Goal:

I Will Achieve This Goal Because:

Today I Am Doing This Towards My Goal:

The Spiritual Work I Did Towards My Big Goal:

The Mental Work I Did Towards My Big Goal:

The Physical Work I Did Today Towards My Big Goal:

It Takes _____ From Me To Achieve This Goal.

I Had To Start _____ So I Can_____.

And I Had To Stop _____So I Can_____.

I Will Not Quit My Goal Because:

LEVELS

Today: _____   Mood: _____

Ultimate Big Goal:

Today's Small Goal Towards The Ultimate Big Goal:

I Will Achieve This Goal Because:

Today I Am Doing This Towards My Goal:

The Spiritual Work I Did Towards My Big Goal:

The Mental Work I Did Towards My Big Goal:

The Physical Work I Did Today Towards My Big Goal:

It Takes _____ From Me To Achieve This Goal.

I Had To Start _____ So I Can_____.

And I Had To Stop _____So I Can_____.

I Will Not Quit My Goal Because:

LEVELS

Today: _____   Mood: _____

Ultimate Big Goal:

Today's Small Goal Towards The Ultimate Big Goal:

I Will Achieve This Goal Because:

Today I Am Doing This Towards My Goal:

The Spiritual Work I Did Towards My Big Goal:

The Mental Work I Did Towards My Big Goal:

The Physical Work I Did Today Towards My Big Goal:

It Takes _____ From Me To Achieve This Goal.

I Had To Start _____ So I Can_____.

And I Had To Stop _____So I Can_____.

I Will Not Quit My Goal Because:

A LOT CAN HAPPEN IN SIX MONTHS.

LEVELS

Today: _____   Mood: _____

Ultimate Big Goal:

Today's Small Goal Towards The Ultimate Big Goal:

I Will Achieve This Goal Because:

Today I Am Doing This Towards My Goal:

The Spiritual Work I Did Towards My Big Goal:

The Mental Work I Did Towards My Big Goal:

The Physical Work I Did Today Towards My Big Goal:

It Takes _____ From Me To Achieve This Goal.

I Had To Start _____ So I Can_____.

And I Had To Stop _____So I Can_____.

I Will Not Quit My Goal Because:

LEVELS

Today: _____   Mood: _____

Ultimate Big Goal:

Today's Small Goal Towards The Ultimate Big Goal:

I Will Achieve This Goal Because:

Today I Am Doing This Towards My Goal:

The Spiritual Work I Did Towards My Big Goal:

The Mental Work I Did Towards My Big Goal:

The Physical Work I Did Today Towards My Big Goal:

It Takes _____ From Me To Achieve This Goal.

I Had To Start _____ So I Can_____.

And I Had To Stop _____So I Can_____.

I Will Not Quit My Goal Because:

LEVELS

Today: _____   Mood: _____

Ultimate Big Goal:

Today's Small Goal Towards The Ultimate Big Goal:

I Will Achieve This Goal Because:

Today I Am Doing This Towards My Goal:

The Spiritual Work I Did Towards My Big Goal:

The Mental Work I Did Towards My Big Goal:

The Physical Work I Did Today Towards My Big Goal:

It Takes _____ From Me To Achieve This Goal.

I Had To Start _____ So I Can_____.

And I Had To Stop _____So I Can_____.

I Will Not Quit My Goal Because:

LEVELS

Today: _____   Mood: _____

Ultimate Big Goal:

Today's Small Goal Towards The Ultimate Big Goal:

I Will Achieve This Goal Because:

Today I Am Doing This Towards My Goal:

The Spiritual Work I Did Towards My Big Goal:

The Mental Work I Did Towards My Big Goal:

The Physical Work I Did Today Towards My Big Goal:

It Takes _____ From Me To Achieve This Goal.

I Had To Start _____ So I Can_____.

And I Had To Stop _____So I Can_____.

I Will Not Quit My Goal Because:

LEVELS

Today: _____   Mood: _____

Ultimate Big Goal:

Today's Small Goal Towards The Ultimate Big Goal:

I Will Achieve This Goal Because:

Today I Am Doing This Towards My Goal:

The Spiritual Work I Did Towards My Big Goal:

The Mental Work I Did Towards My Big Goal:

The Physical Work I Did Today Towards My Big Goal:

It Takes _____ From Me To Achieve This Goal.

I Had To Start _____ So I Can_____.

And I Had To Stop _____So I Can_____.

I Will Not Quit My Goal Because:

LEVELS

Today: Mood:

Ultimate Big Goal:

Today's Small Goal Towards The Ultimate Big Goal:

I Will Achieve This Goal Because:

Today I Am Doing This Towards My Goal:

The Spiritual Work I Did Towards My Big Goal:

The Mental Work I Did Towards My Big Goal:

The Physical Work I Did Today Towards My Big Goal:

It Takes _____ From Me To Achieve This Goal.

I Had To Start _____ So I Can_____.

And I Had To Stop _____So I Can_____.

I Will Not Quit My Goal Because:

KEEP GOING.

LEVELS

Today: Mood:

Ultimate Big Goal:

Today's Small Goal Towards The Ultimate Big Goal:

I Will Achieve This Goal Because:

Today I Am Doing This Towards My Goal:

The Spiritual Work I Did Towards My Big Goal:

The Mental Work I Did Towards My Big Goal:

The Physical Work I Did Today Towards My Big Goal:

It Takes _____ From Me To Achieve This Goal.

I Had To Start _____ So I Can_____.

And I Had To Stop _____So I Can_____.

I Will Not Quit My Goal Because:

Affirmation #103: I am committed to my own success.

LEVELS

Today: _____   Mood: _____

Ultimate Big Goal:

Today's Small Goal Towards The Ultimate Big Goal:

I Will Achieve This Goal Because:

Today I Am Doing This Towards My Goal:

The Spiritual Work I Did Towards My Big Goal:

The Mental Work I Did Towards My Big Goal:

The Physical Work I Did Today Towards My Big Goal:

It Takes _____ From Me To Achieve This Goal.

I Had To Start _____ So I Can_____.

And I Had To Stop _____So I Can_____.

I Will Not Quit My Goal Because:

LEVELS

Today: Mood:

Ultimate Big Goal:

Today's Small Goal Towards The Ultimate Big Goal:

I Will Achieve This Goal Because:

Today I Am Doing This Towards My Goal:

The Spiritual Work I Did Towards My Big Goal:

The Mental Work I Did Towards My Big Goal:

The Physical Work I Did Today Towards My Big Goal:

It Takes _____ From Me To Achieve This Goal.

I Had To Start _____ So I Can_____.

And I Had To Stop _____So I Can_____.

I Will Not Quit My Goal Because:

I AM SAYING YES TO THIS.

I BUILD IN SILENCE SO PEOPLE DON'T KNOW WHAT TO ATTACK.

LEVELS

Today: Mood:

Ultimate Big Goal:

Today's Small Goal Towards The Ultimate Big Goal:

I Will Achieve This Goal Because:

Today I Am Doing This Towards My Goal:

The Spiritual Work I Did Towards My Big Goal:

The Mental Work I Did Towards My Big Goal:

The Physical Work I Did Today Towards My Big Goal:

It Takes _____ From Me To Achieve This Goal.

I Had To Start _____ So I Can_____.

And I Had To Stop _____So I Can_____.

I Will Not Quit My Goal Because:

LEVELS

Today: _____ Mood: _____

Ultimate Big Goal:

Today's Small Goal Towards The Ultimate Big Goal:

I Will Achieve This Goal Because:

Today I Am Doing This Towards My Goal:

The Spiritual Work I Did Towards My Big Goal:

The Mental Work I Did Towards My Big Goal:

The Physical Work I Did Today Towards My Big Goal:

It Takes _____ From Me To Achieve This Goal.

I Had To Start _____ So I Can_____.

And I Had To Stop _____So I Can_____.

I Will Not Quit My Goal Because:

LEVELS

Today: Mood:

Ultimate Big Goal:

Today's Small Goal Towards The Ultimate Big Goal:

I Will Achieve This Goal Because:

Today I Am Doing This Towards My Goal:

The Spiritual Work I Did Towards My Big Goal:

The Mental Work I Did Towards My Big Goal:

The Physical Work I Did Today Towards My Big Goal:

It Takes _____ From Me To Achieve This Goal.

I Had To Start _____ So I Can_____.

And I Had To Stop _____So I Can_____.

I Will Not Quit My Goal Because:

LEVELS

Today: Mood:

Ultimate Big Goal:

Today's Small Goal Towards The Ultimate Big Goal:

I Will Achieve This Goal Because:

Today I Am Doing This Towards My Goal:

The Spiritual Work I Did Towards My Big Goal:

The Mental Work I Did Towards My Big Goal:

The Physical Work I Did Today Towards My Big Goal:

It Takes _____ From Me To Achieve This Goal.

I Had To Start _____ So I Can_____.

And I Had To Stop _____ So I Can_____.

I Will Not Quit My Goal Because:

LEVELS

Today: _____ Mood: _____

Ultimate Big Goal:

Today's Small Goal Towards The Ultimate Big Goal:

I Will Achieve This Goal Because:

Today I Am Doing This Towards My Goal:

The Spiritual Work I Did Towards My Big Goal:

The Mental Work I Did Towards My Big Goal:

The Physical Work I Did Today Towards My Big Goal:

It Takes _____ From Me To Achieve This Goal.

I Had To Start _____ So I Can_____.

And I Had To Stop _____So I Can_____.

I Will Not Quit My Goal Because:

LEVELS

Today: Mood:

Ultimate Big Goal:

Today's Small Goal Towards The Ultimate Big Goal:

I Will Achieve This Goal Because:

Today I Am Doing This Towards My Goal:

The Spiritual Work I Did Towards My Big Goal:

The Mental Work I Did Towards My Big Goal:

The Physical Work I Did Today Towards My Big Goal:

It Takes _____ From Me To Achieve This Goal.

I Had To Start _____ So I Can_____.

And I Had To Stop _____So I Can_____.

I Will Not Quit My Goal Because:

LEVELS

Today: _____ Mood: _____

Ultimate Big Goal:

Today's Small Goal Towards The Ultimate Big Goal:

I Will Achieve This Goal Because:

Today I Am Doing This Towards My Goal:

The Spiritual Work I Did Towards My Big Goal:

The Mental Work I Did Towards My Big Goal:

The Physical Work I Did Today Towards My Big Goal:

It Takes _____ From Me To Achieve This Goal.

I Had To Start _____ So I Can_____.

And I Had To Stop _____So I Can_____.

I Will Not Quit My Goal Because:

NO HURDLE OR STORM WILL STOP ME FROM REACHING MY GOAL. WHATEVER'S TRYING TO STOP ME IS GOING TO HAVE TO TRY HARDER.

LEVELS

Today: _____   Mood: _____

Ultimate Big Goal:

Today's Small Goal Towards The Ultimate Big Goal:

I Will Achieve This Goal Because:

Today I Am Doing This Towards My Goal:

The Spiritual Work I Did Towards My Big Goal:

The Mental Work I Did Towards My Big Goal:

The Physical Work I Did Today Towards My Big Goal:

It Takes _____ From Me To Achieve This Goal.

I Had To Start _____ So I Can_____.

And I Had To Stop _____So I Can_____.

I Will Not Quit My Goal Because:

LEVELS

Today: Mood:

Ultimate Big Goal:

Today's Small Goal Towards The Ultimate Big Goal:

I Will Achieve This Goal Because:

Today I Am Doing This Towards My Goal:

The Spiritual Work I Did Towards My Big Goal:

The Mental Work I Did Towards My Big Goal:

The Physical Work I Did Today Towards My Big Goal:

It Takes _____ From Me To Achieve This Goal.

I Had To Start _____ So I Can_____.

And I Had To Stop _____So I Can_____.

I Will Not Quit My Goal Because:

Affirmation #114: I can achieve whatever I want.

LEVELS

Today: _____   Mood: _____

Ultimate Big Goal:

Today's Small Goal Towards The Ultimate Big Goal:

I Will Achieve This Goal Because:

Today I Am Doing This Towards My Goal:

The Spiritual Work I Did Towards My Big Goal:

The Mental Work I Did Towards My Big Goal:

The Physical Work I Did Today Towards My Big Goal:

It Takes _____ From Me To Achieve This Goal.

I Had To Start _____ So I Can_____.

And I Had To Stop _____So I Can_____.

I Will Not Quit My Goal Because:

LEVELS

Today: _____ Mood: _____

Ultimate Big Goal:

Today's Small Goal Towards The Ultimate Big Goal:

I Will Achieve This Goal Because:

Today I Am Doing This Towards My Goal:

The Spiritual Work I Did Towards My Big Goal:

The Mental Work I Did Towards My Big Goal:

The Physical Work I Did Today Towards My Big Goal:

It Takes _____ From Me To Achieve This Goal.

I Had To Start _____ So I Can_____.

And I Had To Stop _____So I Can_____.

I Will Not Quit My Goal Because:

LEVELS

Today: Mood:

Ultimate Big Goal:

Today's Small Goal Towards The Ultimate Big Goal:

I Will Achieve This Goal Because:

Today I Am Doing This Towards My Goal:

The Spiritual Work I Did Towards My Big Goal:

The Mental Work I Did Towards My Big Goal:

The Physical Work I Did Today Towards My Big Goal:

It Takes _____ From Me To Achieve This Goal.

I Had To Start _____ So I Can_____.

And I Had To Stop _____So I Can_____.

I Will Not Quit My Goal Because:

LEVELS

Today: _____   Mood: _____

Ultimate Big Goal:

Today's Small Goal Towards The Ultimate Big Goal:

I Will Achieve This Goal Because:

Today I Am Doing This Towards My Goal:

The Spiritual Work I Did Towards My Big Goal:

The Mental Work I Did Towards My Big Goal:

The Physical Work I Did Today Towards My Big Goal:

It Takes _____ From Me To Achieve This Goal.

I Had To Start _____ So I Can_____.

And I Had To Stop _____So I Can_____.

I Will Not Quit My Goal Because:

LEVELS

Today: _____ Mood: _____

Ultimate Big Goal:

Today's Small Goal Towards The Ultimate Big Goal:

I Will Achieve This Goal Because:

Today I Am Doing This Towards My Goal:

The Spiritual Work I Did Towards My Big Goal:

The Mental Work I Did Towards My Big Goal:

The Physical Work I Did Today Towards My Big Goal:

It Takes _____ From Me To Achieve This Goal.

I Had To Start _____ So I Can_____.

And I Had To Stop _____So I Can_____.

I Will Not Quit My Goal Because:

BECAUSE I AM GREAT, I WILL SPEND MY LIFE DOING GREAT THINGS. I AM NOT THE NORM.

LEVELS

Today: Mood:

Ultimate Big Goal:

Today's Small Goal Towards The Ultimate Big Goal:

I Will Achieve This Goal Because:

Today I Am Doing This Towards My Goal:

The Spiritual Work I Did Towards My Big Goal:

The Mental Work I Did Towards My Big Goal:

The Physical Work I Did Today Towards My Big Goal:

It Takes _____ From Me To Achieve This Goal.

I Had To Start _____ So I Can_____.

And I Had To Stop _____So I Can_____.

I Will Not Quit My Goal Because:

FOUR MONTH CHECK IN!!!!

WRITE DOWN THE PROGRESS YOU HAVE MADE AND HOW YOU CURRENTLY FEEL. BE SURE TO MENTION WHAT YOU WILL DO DIFFERENTLY TO IMPROVE.

LEVELS

Today: Mood:

Ultimate Big Goal:

Today's Small Goal Towards The Ultimate Big Goal:

I Will Achieve This Goal Because:

Today I Am Doing This Towards My Goal:

The Spiritual Work I Did Towards My Big Goal:

The Mental Work I Did Towards My Big Goal:

The Physical Work I Did Today Towards My Big Goal:

It Takes _____ From Me To Achieve This Goal.

I Had To Start _____ So I Can_____.

And I Had To Stop _____So I Can_____.

I Will Not Quit My Goal Because:

LEVELS

Today: _____ Mood: _____

Ultimate Big Goal:

Today's Small Goal Towards The Ultimate Big Goal:

I Will Achieve This Goal Because:

Today I Am Doing This Towards My Goal:

The Spiritual Work I Did Towards My Big Goal:

The Mental Work I Did Towards My Big Goal:

The Physical Work I Did Today Towards My Big Goal:

It Takes _____ From Me To Achieve This Goal.

I Had To Start _____ So I Can_____.

And I Had To Stop _____So I Can_____.

I Will Not Quit My Goal Because:

LEVELS

Today: _____   Mood: _____

Ultimate Big Goal:

Today's Small Goal Towards The Ultimate Big Goal:

I Will Achieve This Goal Because:

Today I Am Doing This Towards My Goal:

The Spiritual Work I Did Towards My Big Goal:

The Mental Work I Did Towards My Big Goal:

The Physical Work I Did Today Towards My Big Goal:

It Takes _____ From Me To Achieve This Goal.

I Had To Start _____ So I Can_____.

And I Had To Stop _____So I Can_____.

I Will Not Quit My Goal Because:

LEVELS

Today: _____   Mood: _____

Ultimate Big Goal:

Today's Small Goal Towards The Ultimate Big Goal:

I Will Achieve This Goal Because:

Today I Am Doing This Towards My Goal:

The Spiritual Work I Did Towards My Big Goal:

The Mental Work I Did Towards My Big Goal:

The Physical Work I Did Today Towards My Big Goal:

It Takes _____ From Me To Achieve This Goal.

I Had To Start _____ So I Can_____.

And I Had To Stop _____So I Can_____.

I Will Not Quit My Goal Because:

MY NEXT MOVE STAYS PRIVATE.

GREATNESS IS A PROCESS.

LEVELS

Today: _____   Mood: _____

Ultimate Big Goal:

Today's Small Goal Towards The Ultimate Big Goal:

I Will Achieve This Goal Because:

Today I Am Doing This Towards My Goal:

The Spiritual Work I Did Towards My Big Goal:

The Mental Work I Did Towards My Big Goal:

The Physical Work I Did Today Towards My Big Goal:

It Takes _____ From Me To Achieve This Goal.

I Had To Start _____ So I Can_____.

And I Had To Stop _____So I Can_____.

I Will Not Quit My Goal Because:

LEVELS

Today: _____   Mood: _____

Ultimate Big Goal:

Today's Small Goal Towards The Ultimate Big Goal:

I Will Achieve This Goal Because:

Today I Am Doing This Towards My Goal:

The Spiritual Work I Did Towards My Big Goal:

The Mental Work I Did Towards My Big Goal:

The Physical Work I Did Today Towards My Big Goal:

It Takes _____ From Me To Achieve This Goal.

I Had To Start _____ So I Can_____.

And I Had To Stop _____ So I Can_____.

I Will Not Quit My Goal Because:

LEVELS

Today: _____ Mood: _____

Ultimate Big Goal:

Today's Small Goal Towards The Ultimate Big Goal:

I Will Achieve This Goal Because:

Today I Am Doing This Towards My Goal:

The Spiritual Work I Did Towards My Big Goal:

The Mental Work I Did Towards My Big Goal:

The Physical Work I Did Today Towards My Big Goal:

It Takes _____ From Me To Achieve This Goal.

I Had To Start _____ So I Can_____.

And I Had To Stop _____So I Can_____.

I Will Not Quit My Goal Because:

IT'S TIME FOR ME TO GLOW UP.

LEVELS

Today: _____ Mood: _____

Ultimate Big Goal:

Today's Small Goal Towards The Ultimate Big Goal:

I Will Achieve This Goal Because:

Today I Am Doing This Towards My Goal:

The Spiritual Work I Did Towards My Big Goal:

The Mental Work I Did Towards My Big Goal:

The Physical Work I Did Today Towards My Big Goal:

It Takes _____ From Me To Achieve This Goal.

I Had To Start _____ So I Can_____.

And I Had To Stop _____So I Can_____.

I Will Not Quit My Goal Because:

LEVELS

Today: Mood:

Ultimate Big Goal:

Today's Small Goal Towards The Ultimate Big Goal:

I Will Achieve This Goal Because:

Today I Am Doing This Towards My Goal:

The Spiritual Work I Did Towards My Big Goal:

The Mental Work I Did Towards My Big Goal:

The Physical Work I Did Today Towards My Big Goal:

It Takes _____ From Me To Achieve This Goal.

I Had To Start _____ So I Can_____.

And I Had To Stop _____So I Can_____.

I Will Not Quit My Goal Because:

    Affirmation #129: I inspire others to be their best self.

LEVELS

Today: _____ Mood: _____

Ultimate Big Goal:

Today's Small Goal Towards The Ultimate Big Goal:

I Will Achieve This Goal Because:

Today I Am Doing This Towards My Goal:

The Spiritual Work I Did Towards My Big Goal:

The Mental Work I Did Towards My Big Goal:

The Physical Work I Did Today Towards My Big Goal:

It Takes _____ From Me To Achieve This Goal.

I Had To Start _____ So I Can_____.

And I Had To Stop _____So I Can_____.

I Will Not Quit My Goal Because:

LEVELS

Today: Mood:

Ultimate Big Goal:

Today's Small Goal Towards The Ultimate Big Goal:

I Will Achieve This Goal Because:

Today I Am Doing This Towards My Goal:

The Spiritual Work I Did Towards My Big Goal:

The Mental Work I Did Towards My Big Goal:

The Physical Work I Did Today Towards My Big Goal:

It Takes _____ From Me To Achieve This Goal.

I Had To Start _____ So I Can_____.

And I Had To Stop _____So I Can_____.

I Will Not Quit My Goal Because:

LEVELS

Today: Mood:

Ultimate Big Goal:

Today's Small Goal Towards The Ultimate Big Goal:

I Will Achieve This Goal Because:

Today I Am Doing This Towards My Goal:

The Spiritual Work I Did Towards My Big Goal:

The Mental Work I Did Towards My Big Goal:

The Physical Work I Did Today Towards My Big Goal:

It Takes _____ From Me To Achieve This Goal.

I Had To Start _____ So I Can_____.

And I Had To Stop _____So I Can_____.

I Will Not Quit My Goal Because:

LEVELS

Today: _____   Mood: _____

Ultimate Big Goal:

Today's Small Goal Towards The Ultimate Big Goal:

I Will Achieve This Goal Because:

Today I Am Doing This Towards My Goal:

The Spiritual Work I Did Towards My Big Goal:

The Mental Work I Did Towards My Big Goal:

The Physical Work I Did Today Towards My Big Goal:

It Takes _____ From Me To Achieve This Goal.

I Had To Start _____ So I Can_____.

And I Had To Stop _____So I Can_____.

I Will Not Quit My Goal Because:

I FAITH IT TO MAKE IT.

LEVELS

Today: Mood:

Ultimate Big Goal:

Today's Small Goal Towards The Ultimate Big Goal:

I Will Achieve This Goal Because:

Today I Am Doing This Towards My Goal:

The Spiritual Work I Did Towards My Big Goal:

The Mental Work I Did Towards My Big Goal:

The Physical Work I Did Today Towards My Big Goal:

It Takes _____ From Me To Achieve This Goal.

I Had To Start _____ So I Can_____.

And I Had To Stop _____So I Can_____.

I Will Not Quit My Goal Because:

LEVELS

Today: _____   Mood: _____

Ultimate Big Goal:

Today's Small Goal Towards The Ultimate Big Goal:

I Will Achieve This Goal Because:

Today I Am Doing This Towards My Goal:

The Spiritual Work I Did Towards My Big Goal:

The Mental Work I Did Towards My Big Goal:

The Physical Work I Did Today Towards My Big Goal:

It Takes _____ From Me To Achieve This Goal.

I Had To Start _____ So I Can_____.

And I Had To Stop _____ So I Can_____.

I Will Not Quit My Goal Because:

LEVELS

Today: _____   Mood: _____

Ultimate Big Goal:

Today's Small Goal Towards The Ultimate Big Goal:

I Will Achieve This Goal Because:

Today I Am Doing This Towards My Goal:

The Spiritual Work I Did Towards My Big Goal:

The Mental Work I Did Towards My Big Goal:

The Physical Work I Did Today Towards My Big Goal:

It Takes _____ From Me To Achieve This Goal.

I Had To Start _____ So I Can_____.

And I Had To Stop _____So I Can_____.

I Will Not Quit My Goal Because:

Affirmation #136: I am the most beautiful person I know.

LEVELS

Today: Mood:

Ultimate Big Goal:

Today's Small Goal Towards The Ultimate Big Goal:

I Will Achieve This Goal Because:

Today I Am Doing This Towards My Goal:

The Spiritual Work I Did Towards My Big Goal:

The Mental Work I Did Towards My Big Goal:

The Physical Work I Did Today Towards My Big Goal:

It Takes _____ From Me To Achieve This Goal.

I Had To Start _____ So I Can_____.

And I Had To Stop _____So I Can_____.

I Will Not Quit My Goal Because:

IS ANYTHING TOO HARD FOR GOD? THEN YOU MUST KNOW I AM GOOD.

LEVELS

Today: _____ Mood: _____

Ultimate Big Goal:

Today's Small Goal Towards The Ultimate Big Goal:

I Will Achieve This Goal Because:

Today I Am Doing This Towards My Goal:

The Spiritual Work I Did Towards My Big Goal:

The Mental Work I Did Towards My Big Goal:

The Physical Work I Did Today Towards My Big Goal:

It Takes _____ From Me To Achieve This Goal.

I Had To Start _____ So I Can_____.

And I Had To Stop _____So I Can_____.

I Will Not Quit My Goal Because:

LEVELS

Today: Mood:

Ultimate Big Goal:

Today's Small Goal Towards The Ultimate Big Goal:

I Will Achieve This Goal Because:

Today I Am Doing This Towards My Goal:

The Spiritual Work I Did Towards My Big Goal:

The Mental Work I Did Towards My Big Goal:

The Physical Work I Did Today Towards My Big Goal:

It Takes _____ From Me To Achieve This Goal.

I Had To Start _____ So I Can_____.

And I Had To Stop _____So I Can_____.

I Will Not Quit My Goal Because:

LEVELS

Today: Mood:

Ultimate Big Goal:

Today's Small Goal Towards The Ultimate Big Goal:

I Will Achieve This Goal Because:

Today I Am Doing This Towards My Goal:

The Spiritual Work I Did Towards My Big Goal:

The Mental Work I Did Towards My Big Goal:

The Physical Work I Did Today Towards My Big Goal:

It Takes _____ From Me To Achieve This Goal.

I Had To Start _____ So I Can_____.

And I Had To Stop _____So I Can_____.

I Will Not Quit My Goal Because:

LEVELS

Today: _____ Mood: _____

Ultimate Big Goal:

Today's Small Goal Towards The Ultimate Big Goal:

I Will Achieve This Goal Because:

Today I Am Doing This Towards My Goal:

The Spiritual Work I Did Towards My Big Goal:

The Mental Work I Did Towards My Big Goal:

The Physical Work I Did Today Towards My Big Goal:

It Takes _____ From Me To Achieve This Goal.

I Had To Start _____ So I Can_____.

And I Had To Stop _____ So I Can_____.

I Will Not Quit My Goal Because:

Affirmation #141: I deserve what's right. I dserve what's right. I deserve what's right.

LEVELS

Today: Mood:

Ultimate Big Goal:

Today's Small Goal Towards The Ultimate Big Goal:

I Will Achieve This Goal Because:

Today I Am Doing This Towards My Goal:

The Spiritual Work I Did Towards My Big Goal:

The Mental Work I Did Towards My Big Goal:

The Physical Work I Did Today Towards My Big Goal:

It Takes _____ From Me To Achieve This Goal.

I Had To Start _____ So I Can_____.

And I Had To Stop _____So I Can_____.

I Will Not Quit My Goal Because:

LEVELS

Today: Mood:

Ultimate Big Goal:

Today's Small Goal Towards The Ultimate Big Goal:

I Will Achieve This Goal Because:

Today I Am Doing This Towards My Goal:

The Spiritual Work I Did Towards My Big Goal:

The Mental Work I Did Towards My Big Goal:

The Physical Work I Did Today Towards My Big Goal:

It Takes _____ From Me To Achieve This Goal.

I Had To Start _____ So I Can_____.

And I Had To Stop _____So I Can_____.

I Will Not Quit My Goal Because:

LEVELS

Today: Mood:

Ultimate Big Goal:

Today's Small Goal Towards The Ultimate Big Goal:

I Will Achieve This Goal Because:

Today I Am Doing This Towards My Goal:

The Spiritual Work I Did Towards My Big Goal:

The Mental Work I Did Towards My Big Goal:

The Physical Work I Did Today Towards My Big Goal:

It Takes _____ From Me To Achieve This Goal.

I Had To Start _____ So I Can_____.

And I Had To Stop _____So I Can_____.

I Will Not Quit My Goal Because:

LEVELS

Today: _____   Mood: _____

Ultimate Big Goal:

Today's Small Goal Towards The Ultimate Big Goal:

I Will Achieve This Goal Because:

Today I Am Doing This Towards My Goal:

The Spiritual Work I Did Towards My Big Goal:

The Mental Work I Did Towards My Big Goal:

The Physical Work I Did Today Towards My Big Goal:

It Takes _____ From Me To Achieve This Goal.

I Had To Start _____ So I Can_____.

And I Had To Stop _____So I Can_____.

I Will Not Quit My Goal Because:

I LIKE TO SEE OTHERS WIN. THAT'S HOW I WIN.

LEVELS

Today: _____ Mood: _____

Ultimate Big Goal:

Today's Small Goal Towards The Ultimate Big Goal:

I Will Achieve This Goal Because:

Today I Am Doing This Towards My Goal:

The Spiritual Work I Did Towards My Big Goal:

The Mental Work I Did Towards My Big Goal:

The Physical Work I Did Today Towards My Big Goal:

It Takes _____ From Me To Achieve This Goal.

I Had To Start _____ So I Can_____.

And I Had To Stop _____So I Can_____.

I Will Not Quit My Goal Because:

Affirmation #146: I am safe and protected by God.

LEVELS

Today: Mood:

Ultimate Big Goal:

Today's Small Goal Towards The Ultimate Big Goal:

I Will Achieve This Goal Because:

Today I Am Doing This Towards My Goal:

The Spiritual Work I Did Towards My Big Goal:

The Mental Work I Did Towards My Big Goal:

The Physical Work I Did Today Towards My Big Goal:

It Takes _____ From Me To Achieve This Goal.

I Had To Start _____ So I Can_____.

And I Had To Stop _____So I Can_____.

I Will Not Quit My Goal Because:

LEVELS

Today: _____ Mood: _____

Ultimate Big Goal:

Today's Small Goal Towards The Ultimate Big Goal:

I Will Achieve This Goal Because:

Today I Am Doing This Towards My Goal:

The Spiritual Work I Did Towards My Big Goal:

The Mental Work I Did Towards My Big Goal:

The Physical Work I Did Today Towards My Big Goal:

It Takes _____ From Me To Achieve This Goal.

I Had To Start _____ So I Can_____.

And I Had To Stop _____So I Can_____.

I Will Not Quit My Goal Because:

LEVELS

Today: _____ Mood: _____

Ultimate Big Goal:

Today's Small Goal Towards The Ultimate Big Goal:

I Will Achieve This Goal Because:

Today I Am Doing This Towards My Goal:

The Spiritual Work I Did Towards My Big Goal:

The Mental Work I Did Towards My Big Goal:

The Physical Work I Did Today Towards My Big Goal:

It Takes _____ From Me To Achieve This Goal.

I Had To Start _____ So I Can_____.

And I Had To Stop _____So I Can_____.

I Will Not Quit My Goal Because:

LEVELS

Today: Mood:

Ultimate Big Goal:

Today's Small Goal Towards The Ultimate Big Goal:

I Will Achieve This Goal Because:

Today I Am Doing This Towards My Goal:

The Spiritual Work I Did Towards My Big Goal:

The Mental Work I Did Towards My Big Goal:

The Physical Work I Did Today Towards My Big Goal:

It Takes _____ From Me To Achieve This Goal.

I Had To Start _____ So I Can_____.

And I Had To Stop _____So I Can_____.

I Will Not Quit My Goal Because:

           Affirmation #150: I am full of vitality.

I FALL DOWN AND THAN I GET BACK UP. THAT'S THE PART OF MY STORY THAT SCARES THEM.

LEVELS

Today: _____   Mood: _____

Ultimate Big Goal:

Today's Small Goal Towards The Ultimate Big Goal:

I Will Achieve This Goal Because:

Today I Am Doing This Towards My Goal:

The Spiritual Work I Did Towards My Big Goal:

The Mental Work I Did Towards My Big Goal:

The Physical Work I Did Today Towards My Big Goal:

It Takes _____ From Me To Achieve This Goal.

I Had To Start _____ So I Can_____.

And I Had To Stop _____So I Can_____.

I Will Not Quit My Goal Because:

LEVELS

Today: Mood:

Ultimate Big Goal:

Today's Small Goal Towards The Ultimate Big Goal:

I Will Achieve This Goal Because:

Today I Am Doing This Towards My Goal:

The Spiritual Work I Did Towards My Big Goal:

The Mental Work I Did Towards My Big Goal:

The Physical Work I Did Today Towards My Big Goal:

It Takes _____ From Me To Achieve This Goal.

I Had To Start _____ So I Can_____.

And I Had To Stop _____So I Can_____.

I Will Not Quit My Goal Because:

LEVELS

Today: Mood:

Ultimate Big Goal:

Today's Small Goal Towards The Ultimate Big Goal:

I Will Achieve This Goal Because:

Today I Am Doing This Towards My Goal:

The Spiritual Work I Did Towards My Big Goal:

The Mental Work I Did Towards My Big Goal:

The Physical Work I Did Today Towards My Big Goal:

It Takes _____ From Me To Achieve This Goal.

I Had To Start _____ So I Can_____.

And I Had To Stop _____So I Can_____.

I Will Not Quit My Goal Because:

LEVELS

Today: Mood:

Ultimate Big Goal:

Today's Small Goal Towards The Ultimate Big Goal:

I Will Achieve This Goal Because:

Today I Am Doing This Towards My Goal:

The Spiritual Work I Did Towards My Big Goal:

The Mental Work I Did Towards My Big Goal:

The Physical Work I Did Today Towards My Big Goal:

It Takes _____ From Me To Achieve This Goal.

I Had To Start _____ So I Can_____.

And I Had To Stop _____So I Can_____.

I Will Not Quit My Goal Because:

LEVELS

Today: Mood:

Ultimate Big Goal:

Today's Small Goal Towards The Ultimate Big Goal:

I Will Achieve This Goal Because:

Today I Am Doing This Towards My Goal:

The Spiritual Work I Did Towards My Big Goal:

The Mental Work I Did Towards My Big Goal:

The Physical Work I Did Today Towards My Big Goal:

It Takes _____ From Me To Achieve This Goal.

I Had To Start _____ So I Can_____.

And I Had To Stop _____So I Can_____.

I Will Not Quit My Goal Because:

NO ONE CAN STOP ME.

I DON'T SETTLE IN LIFE, IN LOVE OR IN MY PURPOSE. I JUST DON'T SETTLE.

LEVELS

Today: _____ Mood: _____

Ultimate Big Goal:

Today's Small Goal Towards The Ultimate Big Goal:

I Will Achieve This Goal Because:

Today I Am Doing This Towards My Goal:

The Spiritual Work I Did Towards My Big Goal:

The Mental Work I Did Towards My Big Goal:

The Physical Work I Did Today Towards My Big Goal:

It Takes _____ From Me To Achieve This Goal.

I Had To Start _____ So I Can_____.

And I Had To Stop _____So I Can_____.

I Will Not Quit My Goal Because:

LEVELS

Today: _____ Mood: _____

Ultimate Big Goal:

Today's Small Goal Towards The Ultimate Big Goal:

I Will Achieve This Goal Because:

Today I Am Doing This Towards My Goal:

The Spiritual Work I Did Towards My Big Goal:

The Mental Work I Did Towards My Big Goal:

The Physical Work I Did Today Towards My Big Goal:

It Takes _____ From Me To Achieve This Goal.

I Had To Start _____ So I Can_____.

And I Had To Stop _____So I Can_____.

I Will Not Quit My Goal Because:

LEVELS

Today: Mood:

Ultimate Big Goal:

Today's Small Goal Towards The Ultimate Big Goal:

I Will Achieve This Goal Because:

Today I Am Doing This Towards My Goal:

The Spiritual Work I Did Towards My Big Goal:

The Mental Work I Did Towards My Big Goal:

The Physical Work I Did Today Towards My Big Goal:

It Takes _____ From Me To Achieve This Goal.

I Had To Start _____ So I Can_____.

And I Had To Stop _____So I Can_____.

I Will Not Quit My Goal Because:

LEVELS

Today: Mood:

Ultimate Big Goal:

Today's Small Goal Towards The Ultimate Big Goal:

I Will Achieve This Goal Because:

Today I Am Doing This Towards My Goal:

The Spiritual Work I Did Towards My Big Goal:

The Mental Work I Did Towards My Big Goal:

The Physical Work I Did Today Towards My Big Goal:

It Takes _____ From Me To Achieve This Goal.

I Had To Start _____ So I Can_____.

And I Had To Stop _____So I Can_____.

I Will Not Quit My Goal Because:

Affirmation #159: I am choosing to live in my truth because that is what sets me free.

LEVELS

Today: _____   Mood: _____

Ultimate Big Goal:

Today's Small Goal Towards The Ultimate Big Goal:

I Will Achieve This Goal Because:

Today I Am Doing This Towards My Goal:

The Spiritual Work I Did Towards My Big Goal:

The Mental Work I Did Towards My Big Goal:

The Physical Work I Did Today Towards My Big Goal:

It Takes _____ From Me To Achieve This Goal.

I Had To Start _____ So I Can_____.

And I Had To Stop _____So I Can_____.

I Will Not Quit My Goal Because:

GREATER IS COMING....

LEVELS

Today: Mood:

Ultimate Big Goal:

Today's Small Goal Towards The Ultimate Big Goal:

I Will Achieve This Goal Because:

Today I Am Doing This Towards My Goal:

The Spiritual Work I Did Towards My Big Goal:

The Mental Work I Did Towards My Big Goal:

The Physical Work I Did Today Towards My Big Goal:

It Takes _____ From Me To Achieve This Goal.

I Had To Start _____ So I Can_____.

And I Had To Stop _____So I Can_____.

I Will Not Quit My Goal Because:

LEVELS

Today: Mood:

Ultimate Big Goal:

Today's Small Goal Towards The Ultimate Big Goal:

I Will Achieve This Goal Because:

Today I Am Doing This Towards My Goal:

The Spiritual Work I Did Towards My Big Goal:

The Mental Work I Did Towards My Big Goal:

The Physical Work I Did Today Towards My Big Goal:

It Takes _____ From Me To Achieve This Goal.

I Had To Start _____ So I Can_____.

And I Had To Stop _____So I Can_____.

I Will Not Quit My Goal Because:

LEVELS

Today: _____   Mood: _____

Ultimate Big Goal:

Today's Small Goal Towards The Ultimate Big Goal:

I Will Achieve This Goal Because:

Today I Am Doing This Towards My Goal:

The Spiritual Work I Did Towards My Big Goal:

The Mental Work I Did Towards My Big Goal:

The Physical Work I Did Today Towards My Big Goal:

It Takes _____ From Me To Achieve This Goal.

I Had To Start _____ So I Can_____.

And I Had To Stop _____So I Can_____.

I Will Not Quit My Goal Because:

LEVELS

Today: _____ Mood: _____

Ultimate Big Goal:

Today's Small Goal Towards The Ultimate Big Goal:

I Will Achieve This Goal Because:

Today I Am Doing This Towards My Goal:

The Spiritual Work I Did Towards My Big Goal:

The Mental Work I Did Towards My Big Goal:

The Physical Work I Did Today Towards My Big Goal:

It Takes _____ From Me To Achieve This Goal.

I Had To Start _____ So I Can_____.

And I Had To Stop _____So I Can_____.

I Will Not Quit My Goal Because:

LEVELS

Today: _____   Mood: _____

Ultimate Big Goal:

Today's Small Goal Towards The Ultimate Big Goal:

I Will Achieve This Goal Because:

Today I Am Doing This Towards My Goal:

The Spiritual Work I Did Towards My Big Goal:

The Mental Work I Did Towards My Big Goal:

The Physical Work I Did Today Towards My Big Goal:

It Takes _____ From Me To Achieve This Goal.

I Had To Start _____ So I Can_____.

And I Had To Stop _____So I Can_____.

I Will Not Quit My Goal Because:

LEVELS

Today: Mood:

Ultimate Big Goal:

Today's Small Goal Towards The Ultimate Big Goal:

I Will Achieve This Goal Because:

Today I Am Doing This Towards My Goal:

The Spiritual Work I Did Towards My Big Goal:

The Mental Work I Did Towards My Big Goal:

The Physical Work I Did Today Towards My Big Goal:

It Takes _____ From Me To Achieve This Goal.

I Had To Start _____ So I Can_____.

And I Had To Stop _____So I Can_____.

I Will Not Quit My Goal Because:

Affirmation #166: The only thing I see are solutions. I am not easily

WATCH MY ACTIONS... THEY BACK UP MY WORDS.

LEVELS

Today: Mood:

Ultimate Big Goal:

Today's Small Goal Towards The Ultimate Big Goal:

I Will Achieve This Goal Because:

Today I Am Doing This Towards My Goal:

The Spiritual Work I Did Towards My Big Goal:

The Mental Work I Did Towards My Big Goal:

The Physical Work I Did Today Towards My Big Goal:

It Takes _____ From Me To Achieve This Goal.

I Had To Start _____ So I Can_____.

And I Had To Stop _____So I Can_____.

I Will Not Quit My Goal Because:

would cause me

LEVELS

Today: Mood:

Ultimate Big Goal:

Today's Small Goal Towards The Ultimate Big Goal:

I Will Achieve This Goal Because:

Today I Am Doing This Towards My Goal:

The Spiritual Work I Did Towards My Big Goal:

The Mental Work I Did Towards My Big Goal:

The Physical Work I Did Today Towards My Big Goal:

It Takes _____ From Me To Achieve This Goal.

I Had To Start _____ So I Can_____.

And I Had To Stop _____ So I Can_____.

I Will Not Quit My Goal Because:

LEVELS

Today: Mood:

Ultimate Big Goal:

Today's Small Goal Towards The Ultimate Big Goal:

I Will Achieve This Goal Because:

Today I Am Doing This Towards My Goal:

The Spiritual Work I Did Towards My Big Goal:

The Mental Work I Did Towards My Big Goal:

The Physical Work I Did Today Towards My Big Goal:

It Takes _____ From Me To Achieve This Goal.

I Had To Start _____ So I Can_____.

And I Had To Stop _____So I Can_____.

I Will Not Quit My Goal Because:

Affirmation #169: I am expecting miracles, transformations, and pure joy as a result to achieving my goals.

I'M DOING THE SPIRITUAL WORK. I'M DOING THE MENTAL WORK. I'M DOING THE PHYSICAL WORK. JUST KNOW I'M PUTTING IN THE WORK.

LEVELS

Today: _____ Mood: _____

Ultimate Big Goal:

Today's Small Goal Towards The Ultimate Big Goal:

I Will Achieve This Goal Because:

Today I Am Doing This Towards My Goal:

The Spiritual Work I Did Towards My Big Goal:

The Mental Work I Did Towards My Big Goal:

The Physical Work I Did Today Towards My Big Goal:

It Takes _____ From Me To Achieve This Goal.

I Had To Start _____ So I Can_____.

And I Had To Stop _____So I Can_____.

I Will Not Quit My Goal Because:

LEVELS

Today: _____ Mood: _____

Ultimate Big Goal:

Today's Small Goal Towards The Ultimate Big Goal:

I Will Achieve This Goal Because:

Today I Am Doing This Towards My Goal:

The Spiritual Work I Did Towards My Big Goal:

The Mental Work I Did Towards My Big Goal:

The Physical Work I Did Today Towards My Big Goal:

It Takes _____ From Me To Achieve This Goal.

I Had To Start _____ So I Can_____.

And I Had To Stop _____So I Can_____.

I Will Not Quit My Goal Because:

LEVELS

Today: Mood:

Ultimate Big Goal:

Today's Small Goal Towards The Ultimate Big Goal:

I Will Achieve This Goal Because:

Today I Am Doing This Towards My Goal:

The Spiritual Work I Did Towards My Big Goal:

The Mental Work I Did Towards My Big Goal:

The Physical Work I Did Today Towards My Big Goal:

It Takes _____ From Me To Achieve This Goal.

I Had To Start _____ So I Can_____.

And I Had To Stop _____So I Can_____.

I Will Not Quit My Goal Because:

LEVELS

Today: Mood:

Ultimate Big Goal:

Today's Small Goal Towards The Ultimate Big Goal:

I Will Achieve This Goal Because:

Today I Am Doing This Towards My Goal:

The Spiritual Work I Did Towards My Big Goal:

The Mental Work I Did Towards My Big Goal:

The Physical Work I Did Today Towards My Big Goal:

It Takes _____ From Me To Achieve This Goal.

I Had To Start _____ So I Can_____.

And I Had To Stop _____So I Can_____.

I Will Not Quit My Goal Because:

LEVELS

Today: Mood:

Ultimate Big Goal:

Today's Small Goal Towards The Ultimate Big Goal:

I Will Achieve This Goal Because:

Today I Am Doing This Towards My Goal:

The Spiritual Work I Did Towards My Big Goal:

The Mental Work I Did Towards My Big Goal:

The Physical Work I Did Today Towards My Big Goal:

It Takes _____ From Me To Achieve This Goal.

I Had To Start _____ So I Can_____.

And I Had To Stop _____So I Can_____.

I Will Not Quit My Goal Because:

LEVELS

Today: _____   Mood: _____

Ultimate Big Goal:

Today's Small Goal Towards The Ultimate Big Goal:

I Will Achieve This Goal Because:

Today I Am Doing This Towards My Goal:

The Spiritual Work I Did Towards My Big Goal:

The Mental Work I Did Towards My Big Goal:

The Physical Work I Did Today Towards My Big Goal:

It Takes _____ From Me To Achieve This Goal.

I Had To Start _____ So I Can_____.

And I Had To Stop _____So I Can_____.

I Will Not Quit My Goal Because:

PROTECTING MY DREAMS AS I WATCH THEM COME TRUE.

LEVELS

Today: _____   Mood: _____

Ultimate Big Goal:

Today's Small Goal Towards The Ultimate Big Goal:

I Will Achieve This Goal Because:

Today I Am Doing This Towards My Goal:

The Spiritual Work I Did Towards My Big Goal:

The Mental Work I Did Towards My Big Goal:

The Physical Work I Did Today Towards My Big Goal:

It Takes _____ From Me To Achieve This Goal.

I Had To Start _____ So I Can_____.

And I Had To Stop _____ So I Can_____.

I Will Not Quit My Goal Because:

LEVELS

Today: Mood:

Ultimate Big Goal:

Today's Small Goal Towards The Ultimate Big Goal:

I Will Achieve This Goal Because:

Today I Am Doing This Towards My Goal:

The Spiritual Work I Did Towards My Big Goal:

The Mental Work I Did Towards My Big Goal:

The Physical Work I Did Today Towards My Big Goal:

It Takes _____ From Me To Achieve This Goal.

I Had To Start _____ So I Can_____.

And I Had To Stop _____So I Can_____.

I Will Not Quit My Goal Because:

LEVELS

Today: Mood:

Ultimate Big Goal:

Today's Small Goal Towards The Ultimate Big Goal:

I Will Achieve This Goal Because:

Today I Am Doing This Towards My Goal:

The Spiritual Work I Did Towards My Big Goal:

The Mental Work I Did Towards My Big Goal:

The Physical Work I Did Today Towards My Big Goal:

It Takes _____ From Me To Achieve This Goal.

I Had To Start _____ So I Can_____.

And I Had To Stop _____So I Can_____.

I Will Not Quit My Goal Because:

LEVELS

Today: _____ Mood: _____

Ultimate Big Goal:

Today's Small Goal Towards The Ultimate Big Goal:

I Will Achieve This Goal Because:

Today I Am Doing This Towards My Goal:

The Spiritual Work I Did Towards My Big Goal:

The Mental Work I Did Towards My Big Goal:

The Physical Work I Did Today Towards My Big Goal:

It Takes _____ From Me To Achieve This Goal.

I Had To Start _____ So I Can_____.

And I Had To Stop _____So I Can_____.

I Will Not Quit My Goal Because:

Affirmation #179: I have an amazing support system that loves me for me.

LEVELS

Today: Mood:

Ultimate Big Goal:

Today's Small Goal Towards The Ultimate Big Goal:

I Will Achieve This Goal Because:

Today I Am Doing This Towards My Goal:

The Spiritual Work I Did Towards My Big Goal:

The Mental Work I Did Towards My Big Goal:

The Physical Work I Did Today Towards My Big Goal:

It Takes _____ From Me To Achieve This Goal.

I Had To Start _____ So I Can_____.

And I Had To Stop _____So I Can_____.

I Will Not Quit My Goal Because:

SIX MONTH CHECK IN!!!!

ARE YOU ON TRACK?

HOW HAVE THINGS CHANGED FOR YOU?

HOW WILL YOU CONTINUE TO MOVE FORWARD?

Made in the
USA
Middletown, DE